Workbook of Study Guides with Solutions II
Chapters 14-28

to accompany

Fundamental Accounting Principles
Eleventh Edition

Kermit D. Larson
The University of Texas at Austin

William W. Pyle

1987
IRWIN

Homewood, Illinois 60430

1 2 3 4 5 6 7 8 9 0 VK 4 3 2 1 0 9 8 7

To the Student

This booklet is designed to help you review the material covered in Chapters 14–28 of *Fundamental Accounting Principles*, 11th edition. You should understand that the booklet is not intended to substitute for your review of *Fundamental Accounting Principles*. Instead, the objectives of this booklet are as follows:

1. To remind you of important information that is explained in the text. For example, the topical outline of each chapter reminds you of important topics in the chapter. In reading the outline, you should ask yourself whether or not you understand sufficiently the listed topics. If not, you should return to the appropriate chapter in *Fundamental Accounting Principles* and read carefully the portions that explain the topics about which you are unclear.

2. To provide you with a quick means of testing your knowledge of the chapter. If you are unable to correctly answer the "Parts" that follow the chapter outline, you should once again return to the appropriate chapter in *Fundamental Accounting Principles* and review the sections about which you are unclear.

Your best approach to the use of this booklet is as follows:

First, read the learning objectives and ask whether your understanding of the chapter seems adequate for you to accomplish the objectives.

Second, review the topical outline, taking time to think through (describing to yourself) the explanations that would be required to expand the outline. Return to *Fundamental Accounting Principles* to cover areas of weakness.

Third, answer the requirements of the Parts that follow the topical outline. Then check your answers against the solutions that are provided after the Parts.

Fourth, return to *Fundamental Accounting Principles* for further study of the portions of the chapter about which you made errors.

Contents

Contents

14

Partnership Accounting

Your objectives in studying this chapter should include learning how to:

List the characteristics of a partnership and explain the importance of mutual agency and unlimited liability to a person about to become a partner.

Allocate partnership earnings to partners (a) on a stated fractional basis, (b) in the partners' capital ratio, and (c) through the use of salary and interest allowances.

Prepare entries for (a) the sale of a partnership interest, (b) the admission of a new partner by investment, and (c) the retirement of a partner by the withdrawal of partnership assets.

Prepare entries required in the liquidation of a partnership.

Define or explain the words and phrases listed in the chapter Glossary.

Topical Outline

I. Characteristics of a partnership

   A. A voluntary association.

   B. Based on a contract, which should be in writing but may be only orally expressed.

   C. Limited life—death, bankruptcy, or expiration of the contract period automatically end a partnership.

   D. Mutual agency—every partner is an agent of the partnership and can enter into and bind it to any contract within the normal scope of its business.

   E. Unlimited liability—each partner is responsible for payment of all the debts of the partnership if the other partners are unable to pay a share.

II. Limited partnerships

   A. Two classes of partners

      1. General partner(s)—assumes unlimited liability for the debts of the partnership.

      2. Limited partners—have no personal liability beyond their invested amounts.

   B. "General partnership" often used for partnerships in which all the partners have unlimited liability.

III. Partnership accounting

   A. Owners' equity accounts

      1. Capital account for each partner

      2. Withdrawals account for each partner

   B. Measurement and division of earnings

      1. Partners have no legal right to salary, so there is no salary expense for partners.

      2. In the absence of an agreement, partnership earnings and losses are shared equally among the partners.

      3. Methods of sharing partnership earnings:

         a. On a fractional basis.

         b. Based on the ratio of capital investments.

         c. Based on salary and interest allowances with the remainder in a fixed ratio.

      4. Partners can agree to salary and interest allowances when distributing profits to reward unequal contribution of services or capital.

IV. Addition or withdrawal of a partner

   A. Sale of a partnership interest requires that the old partner's capital account be transferred to the new partner's capital account.

   B. Investing in an existing partnership

      1. Partnership assets are increased.

      2. The agreement may involve a bonus to the old partners or to the new partner.

      3. A bonus involves a transfer of capital account balances between the partners.

   C. Withdrawal of a partner depends on the partnership agreement.

      1. Partnership assets may be revalued.

      2. The agreement may result in a partner taking assets of greater or lesser value than his or her book equity.

      3. The capital accounts of the partners may require adjustment to reflect the agreed-upon division of assets when a partner withdraws.

V. Liquidations of partnerships

   A. As assets are sold, gains or losses must be recorded.

   B. Partnership creditors must be paid before partners.

C. If a partner's capital account is not sufficient to absorb his or her share of liquidation losses:
1. He or she must, if possible, contribute assets to the partnership to cover the deficiency.
2. Otherwise, the remaining partners' capital accounts must be charged for the capital deficiency of the defaulting partner.

Part I

Many of the important ideas and concepts discussed in Chapter 14 are reflected in the following list of key terms. Test your understanding of these terms by matching the appropriate definitions with the terms. Record the number identifying the most appropriate definition in the blank space next to each term.

_____ Deficit	_____ Liquidation
_____ General partner	_____ Mutual agency
_____ General partnership	_____ Partnership
_____ Limited partners	_____ Partnership contract
_____ Limited partnership	_____ Unlimited liability of partners

1. The legal characteristic of a partnership whereby each partner is an agent of the partnership and is able to bind the partnership to contracts within the normal scope of the partnership business.

2. The document setting forth the agreed terms under which the members of a partnership will conduct the partnership business.

3. A negative balance in an account.

4. The winding up of a business by converting its assets to cash and distributing the cash to the proper parties.

5. A partner who assumes unlimited liability for the debts of the partnership.

6. A partnership that has two classes of partners, limited partners and one or more general partners.

7. The legal characteristic of a partnership that makes each partner responsible for paying all the debts of the partnership if his or her partners are unable to pay their shares.

8. A partnership in which all partners have unlimited liability for partnership debts.

9. Partners who have no personal liability for debts of the limited partnership beyond the amounts they have invested in the partnership.

10. An association of two or more persons to carry on a business as co-owners for profit.

Part II

Complete the following by filling in the blanks.

1. Partnership accounting is exactly like that of a single proprietorship except for transactions affecting _____.

2. Four advantages of a partnership over the single proprietorship and corporation forms of organization are:

    (a) _____
    _____;

    (b) _____
    _____;

    (c) _____
    _____;

    (d) _____
    _____.

3. A _____ (limited, general) partnership has two classes of partners.

4. Although a partner does not work for either a salary or interest, to be fair in the distribution of partnership earnings, it is often necessary to recognize that the earnings do include a return for _____ and a return on _____.

5. Blake and Dillon are partners who have always shared incomes and losses equally. Hester has sued the partners on a partnership debt and obtained a $12,000 judgment. The partnership and Dillon have no assets; consequently, Hester is attempting to collect the entire $12,000 from Blake. Blake has sufficient assets to pay the judgment but refuses, claiming she is liable for only one half the $12,000. Hester _____ (can, cannot) collect the entire $12,000 from Blake because _____
    _____.

6. Since a partnership is a voluntary association, an individual _____ (can, cannot) be forced against his will to become a partner; and since a partnership is based on a contract, its life is _____.

7. The fact that partners cannot enter into an employer-employee contractual relation with themselves supports the contention held in law and custom that partners work for partnership _____ and not for a salary. Furthermore, partners invest in a partnership for _____ and not for interest.

8. The phrase mutual agency when applied to a partnership means _____
    _____
    _____.

6

9. Jay and Faye are partners in the operation of an insurance agency. Business has been slow, and without consulting Faye, Jay entered into a contract with Rays Limited to purchase three satellite dishes to be sold by the partnership. Faye repudiated the contract. If Rays Limited attempts to hold the partnership liable on the contract, it _____ (can, cannot) do so because _____ _____.

Part III

Flip and Flop began a partnership by investing $14,000 and $10,000, respectively, and during its first year the partnership earned a $21,000 net income. *Required:* Complete the tabulation below to show under the several assumptions the share of each partner in the $21,000 net income.

	Flip's Share	Flop's Share
1. The partners failed to agree as to the method of sharing	$	$
2. The partners had agreed to share in their beginning-of-year investment ratio	$	$
3. The partners had agreed to share by giving an $8,200 per year salary allowance to Flip and a $9,000 per year salary allowance to Flop, plus 10% interest on their beginning-of-year investments, and the remainder equally	$	$

Part IV

1. Assume that the partnership of Flip and Flop (Part III above) earned $14,000 rather than $21,000 and that the partners had agreed to share incomes and losses by giving salary allowances of $8,200 and $9,000 respectively, 10% interest on beginning investments, and the remainder equally. Flip's share of the $14,000 would be $ _____, and Flop's share would be $ _____.

2. Also, if Flip and Flop share incomes and losses as immediately above, and the partnership incurred a $3,800 loss rather than a profit, Flip's share of the loss would be $ _____ and Flop's share would be $ _____.

7

Part V

Use the following balance sheet information to complete the work below.

PINTER, KING AND TODD
Balance Sheet
December 31, 19—

Assets		Owners' Equities	
Cash	$ 8,000	Martin Pinter, capital	$ 9,000
Other assets	19,000	Mike King, capital	9,000
		Harold Todd, capital	9,000
Total assets	$27,000	Total owners' equities	$27,000

1. Martin Pinter has a $9,000 equity in the partnership of Pinter, King and Todd. If with the consent of his partners, he sells his equity to Lee Russell for $9,000, the entry to record the transaction is:

DATE	ACCOUNT TITLES AND EXPLANATION	P.R.	DEBIT	CREDIT

2. If rather than selling the equity for $9,000, Pinter sold it for $10,000, the entry _____ (would, would not) be the same.

Part VI

The condensed balance sheet of Shaw, Greene, and Wilson, who have always shared incomes and losses in a 3:2:1 ratio follows. Wilson plans to leave the partnership. Shaw and Greene plan to continue the business under a new partnership contract.

SHAW, GREENE, AND WILSON
Balance Sheet
December 31, 19—

Assets		Owners' Equities	
Cash	$10,000	Edmund Shaw, capital	$17,000
Other assets	30,000	Bernard Greene, capital	15,000
		Graham Wilson, capital	8,000
Total assets	$40,000	Total owners' equities	$40,000

1. If Wilson takes $8,000 of partnership cash in settlement for his equity, the remaining assets will total $ _____; Shaw's equity in the remaining assets will be $ _____; and Greene's equity will be $ _____.

2. If Wilson takes $9,000 of partnership cash in settlement for his equity, the remaining assets will be $ _____; Shaw's equity in the remaining assets will be $ _____; and Greene's equity will be $ _____.

8

3. If Wilson takes $7,500 of partnership cash in settlement for his equity, the remaining assets will total $ _____ ; Shaw's equity in these assets will be $ _____ ; and Greene's equity will be $ _____ .

Part VII

Wheeler, Carson, and Young, who have operated a partnership for a number of years, sharing incomes and losses equally, are to liquidate. The assets and equities of the partnership just prior to its liquidation are shown in the T-accounts below.

Cash			Accounts Payable		
Dec. 31	9,000			Dec. 31	9,000

Other Assets			Wheeler, Capital		
Dec. 31	29,000			Dec. 31	12,000

Loss or Gain from Realization			Carson, Capital		
				Dec. 31	9,000

			Young, Capital		
				Dec. 31	8,000

1. Make entries directly in the T-accounts to record the sale of the other assets under the assumption that the other assets are sold for $20,000.

2. Make entries directly in the T-accounts to allocate the loss from realization to the partners.

3. Since the creditor claims take precedence over the claims of the partners, make entries in the T-accounts to pay the creditors.

4. Fill in the blanks in the following statements:

At this point in the liquidation of the partnership of Wheeler, Carson, and Young, after losses are shared and the creditors are paid, the balance of the Cash account is

$ _____ and is equal to the sum of the balances of the

_____ accounts. The balances of the partners' capital

accounts are: Wheeler, $ _____ ; Carson, $ _____ ; and

Young $ _____ . Consequently, in a final distribution of cash Wheeler should

receive $ _____ , Carson should receive $ _____ , and

Young should receive $ _____ .

Part I

Deficit	3	Liquidation	4
General partner	5	Mutual agency	1
General partnership	8	Partnership	10
Limited partners	9	Partnership contract	2
Limited partnership	6	Unlimited liability of partners	7

Part II

1. the partners' equities

2. (a) Brings more money and skills together than a single proprietorship
   (b) Is easier to organize than a corporation
   (c) Does not have the corporation's governmental supervision or extra taxation burden
   (d) Allows partners to act freely and without the necessity of stockholders' and directors' meetings, as is required in a corporation

3. limited

4. services, investments

5. can, each partner is unlimitedly liable for the debts of the partnership

6. cannot, limited

7. profits or earnings, profits or earnings

8. each partner is an agent of the partnership and can bind it to contracts

9. cannot, the sale of satellite dishes is not the normal business of an insurance agency

Part III

1. $10,500, $10,500
2. $12,250, $8,750
3. $10,300, $10,700

Part IV

1. $6,800, $7,200
2. ($2,100), ($1,700)

Part V

1. Dec. 31 Martin Pinter, Capital 9,000.00
             Lee Russell, Capital 9,000.00
2. would

Part VI

1. $32,000; $17,000; $15,000.
2. $31,000; $16,400; $14,600.
3. $32,500; $17,300; $15,200.

Part VII

1., 2., and 3.

	Cash				Accounts Payable	
Dec. 31	9,000	Dec. 31	9,000	Dec. 31	9,000	Dec. 31	9,000
31	20,000					

	Other Assets				Wheeler, Capital	
Dec. 31	29,000	Dec. 31	29,000	Dec. 31	3,000	Dec. 31	12,000

	Loss or Gain from Realization				Carson, Capital	
Dec. 31	9,000	Dec. 31	9,000	Dec. 31	3,000	Dec. 31	9,000

					Young, Capital	
				Dec. 31	3,000	Dec. 31	8,000

4. Cash, $20,000, partners' capital. Partners' capital account balances: Wheeler, $9,000; Carson, $6,000; Young, $5,000. Wheeler should receive $9,000; Carson should receive $6,000; and Young should receive $5,000.

15

Organization and Operation of Corporations

Your objectives in studying this chapter should include learning how to:

State the advantages and disadvantages of the corporate form of business organization and explain how a corporation is organized and managed.

Describe the differences in accounting for the owners' equity in a partnership and the stockholders' equity in a corporation.

Record the issuance of par value stock at par or at a premium in exchange for cash or other assets.

Record the issuance of no-par stock with or without a stated value.

Record transactions involving stock subscriptions and explain the effects of subscribed stock on corporation assets and stockholders' equity.

Explain the concept of minimum legal capital and explain why corporation laws governing minimum legal capital were written.

State the differences between common and preferred stocks and explain why preferred stock is issued.

Describe the meaning and significance of par, book, market, and redemption values of corporate stock.

Define or explain the words and phrases listed in the chapter Glossary.

Topical Outline

I. Advantages and disadvantages of the corporate form of business

   A. Advantages:

      1. Separate legal entity—a corporation, through its agents, may conduct business affairs with the same rights, duties, and responsibilities as a person.
      2. Lack of stockholders' liability.
      3. Ease of transferring ownership rights.
      4. Continuity of life—a perpetual life is possible for a successful corporation.
      5. No mutual agency—an individual, acting as a stockholder, cannot bind the corporation to contracts.
      6. Ease of capital assembly—the advantages of the corporate form make it easier for a corporation to raise large amounts of capital.

   B. Disadvantages:

      1. Increased governmental regulation.
      2. Taxation—corporate income is taxed; and when income is distributed to shareholders as dividends, it is taxed a second time.

II. Organizing, managing and accounting for a corporation

   A. Organization costs—normally debited to an asset account and amortized over a period not to exceed 40 years.
   B. Management—stockholders, board of directors and administrative officers.
   C. Accounting—stockholders' equity accounts are divided into contributed capital accounts and retained earnings accounts.

III. Common stock

   A. A corporation may issue no more stock than is authorized by its charter.
   B. Stock may be issued in exchange for cash or other assets.
   C. Par value—an arbitrary value placed on a share of stock which in many states establishes a minimum legal capital.
   D. Premium on stock—the amount of capital contributed by stockholders above the stock's par value.
   E. Discount on stock—the difference between the par value of stock and the amount below par value contributed by stockholders.
   F. No-par stock—a class of stock having no par value.

      1. Advantage is that it may be issued at any price without having a discount liability attached.
      2. A stated value may be placed on no-par stock; the stated value then becomes minimum legal capital and is credited to the no-par stock account at the time the stock is issued.

   G. Subscriptions—in some instances, stock can be purchased on an installment basis.

      1. Subscriptions receivable are reported as assets.
      2. Common stock subscribed is reported in stockholders' equity.

   H. Rights of common stockholders:

      1. The right to vote in stockholders' meetings.
      2. The right to sell or otherwise dispose of their stock.
      3. The right (known as the preemptive right) of first opportunity to purchase any additional shares of common stock issued by the corporation.
      4. The right to share pro rata with other common stockholders in any dividends distributed to common stockholders.
      5. The right to share in any assets remaining after creditors are paid if the corporation is liquidated.

IV. Preferred stock

    A. Preferred stock—so called because of preferences granted to its owners.

        1. Preference as to payment of dividends.

        2. Preference in distribution of assets in a liquidation.

    B. Participating or nonparticipating preferred stock

        1. Participating preferred stock—provides the right to share in dividends above the fixed amount or percentage which is preferred.

        2. Nonparticipating preferred stock—dividends to stock are limited to a fixed maximum amount.

    C. Cumulative or noncumulative preferred stock

        1. Cumulative—any undeclared dividends accumulated annually until paid.

        2. Noncumulative—the right to receive dividends is forfeited in any year that dividends are not declared.

V. Stock values

    A. Redemption value—the amount a corporation agrees to pay to redeem a share of its preferred stock.

    B. Market value—the amount at which a share of stock may be bought or sold.

    C. Book value—the equity represented by one share of stock in the issuing corporation's net assets.

        1. Common stock—total stockholders' equity (less the book value of preferred stock, if any) divided by number of common shares outstanding.

        2. Preferred stock—redemption value (or par value if there is no redemption value) plus any cumulative dividends in arrears divided by number of preferred shares outstanding.

        3. Generally has little bearing upon liquidation value or market value.

16

Part I

Many of the important ideas and concepts discussed in Chapter 15 are reflected in the following list of key terms. Test your understanding of these terms by matching the appropriate definitions with the terms. Record the number identifying the most appropriate definition in the blank space next to each term.

_____	Book value of a share of stock	_____	Organization costs
_____	Common stock	_____	Participating preferred stock
_____	Common stock subscribed	_____	Par value
_____	Cumulative preferred stock	_____	Preemptive right
_____	Discount on stock	_____	Preferred stock
_____	Dividend	_____	Premium on stock
_____	Dividends in arrears	_____	Proxy
_____	Minimum legal capital	_____	Redemption value of stock
_____	Noncumulative preferred stock	_____	Stated value of no-parstock
_____	No-par stock	_____	Stock subscription

1. A contractual commitment to purchase unissued shares of stock and become a stockholder.

2. Stock of a corporation that has only one class of stock; if there is more than one class, the class that has no preferences relative to the corporation's other classes of stock.

3. Unpaid prior period dividends on preferred stock which must be paid before dividends are paid to common stockholders.

4. A legal document that gives an agent of a stockholder the right to vote the stockholder's shares.

5. Unissued common stock for which the issuing corporation has a subscription contract to issue.

6. A preferred stock for which the right to receive dividends is forfeited in any year in which dividends are not declared.

7. The right of common stockholders to protect their proportionate interests in a corporation by having the first opportunity to purchase additional shares of common stock issued by the corporation.

8. A class of stock that does not have an arbitrary (par) value placed on the stock at the time the stock is first authorized.

9. Preferred stock on which undeclared dividends accumulate annually until paid.

10. An amount, established by a corporation's board of directors, that is credited to the no-par stock account at the time the stock is issued.

11. An arbitrary value placed on a share of stock at the time the stock is authorized.

12. Costs of bringing a corporation into existence, such as legal fees, promoters' fees, and amounts paid the state to secure a charter.

13. Preferred stock that has the right to share in dividends above the fixed amount or percentage which is preferred.

14. The amount of capital contributed by stockholders above the stock's par value.

15. The equity represented by one share of stock in the issuing corporation's net assets.

16. A distribution made by a corporation to its stockholders of cash, other assets, or additional shares of the corporation's own stock.

17

17. An amount, as defined by state law, that stockholders must invest in a corporation or be contingently liable to its creditors.

18. Stock the owners of which are granted certain preferences over common stockholders, such as a preference to payment of dividends or in the distribution of assets in a liquidation.

19. The amount a corporation must pay if and when it exercises its right to require the return of a share of preferred stock previously issued by the corporation.

20. The difference between the par value of stock and the amount below par value contributed by stockholders.

Part II

The following statements are either true or false. Place an (X) in the parentheses before each true statement and an (O) before each false one.

1. (   ) The return earned by common stockholders is made larger by issuing preferred stock if the dividends to preferred stock are less than the amount earned through the use of the preferred stockholders' money.

2. (   ) Since the stockholders can always elect a new board of directors, the ultimate control of a corporation rests with its stockholders.

3. (   ) Owners of participating preferred stock have the right to participate in the management of the corporation issuing the stock.

4. (   ) The acts of a corporation must conform with its charter, its bylaws, and the laws of the jurisdiction of its incorporation.

5. (   ) A stockholder owning 51 percent of the stock in a corporation and acting as a stockholder can bind the corporation to contracts that are within the normal scope of the corporation's business.

6. (   ) A corporation director can bind the corporation to contracts that are within the normal scope of the corporation's business.

7. (   ) A corporation comes into existence when its charter is granted.

8. (   ) Final authority in the management of corporation affairs rests with its board of directors.

9. (   ) A corporation may exist forever.

10. (   ) A corporation, as a separate legal entity, is responsible for its own acts and its own debts and its stockholders generally have no liability for either.

11. (   ) Dividends are guaranteed on cumulative preferred stock.

12. (   ) To transfer and sell his or her interest in a corporation, a stockholder must secure permission from the corporation's secretary.

13. (   ) The preemptive right of common stockholders gives them the right to maintain their proportionate interest in a corporation.

14. (   ) The death of a stockholder owning a majority interest in a corporation requires a reorganization and the formation of a new corporation.

18

15. ( ) Stockholders have no right to a dividend until the dividend is declared by the board of directors.

16. ( ) The president of a corporation is usually elected by the stockholders at one of their annual meetings.

17. ( ) Requiring a corporation to have both a registrar and a transfer agent is an example of a division of duties for purposes of control.

18. ( ) The president of a corporation is responsible to its board of directors for management of the corporation's affairs.

Part III

Complete the following by filling in the blanks.

1. Organization costs are classified as a(n) _____ asset from which a corporation will benefit throughout its life. However, due to income tax rules organization costs are commonly written off over the first _____ years of a corporation's life.

2. Laws establishing minimum legal capital requirements were written to protect _____ _____, with the protection resulting from making illegal the payment of any dividends that reduce stockholders' equity below _____ _____.

3. A discount on stock is the difference between _____ and the amount at which stock is issued when the stock is issued at a price below its par value.

4. When stock is issued at a price above its par value, the difference between par and the price at which the stock is issued is called a _____.

5. Advantages claimed for no-par stock are: (a) It maybe issued at any price without ___ _____. (b) Uninformed persons buying such stock are not misled as to the stock's worth by a _____ printed on the certificates.

6. Laws setting minimum legal capital requirements normally require stockholders to invest, in a corporation, assets equal in value to minimum legal capital or be contingently liable to _____ for the deficiency.

7. A preferred stock is so called because of the preferences granted its owners. The two most common preferences are a preference as to _____ _____ and a preference _____ _____.

8. In many jurisdictions when a corporation issues par value stock, it establishes for itself a _____ equal to the par value of the issued stock.

19

9. In addition to its separate legal existence, other advantages of a corporation as a form of business organization are _____

_____

_____

_____

_____.

10. A corporation is said to be a separate legal entity this phrase means that in a legal sense a corporation is _____

_____.

11. Par value is an arbitrary value established for stock and printed on each stock certificate. It has _____ (little, much, nothing) to do with the stock's worth.

Part IV

The stockholders' equity section from Sonar Corporation's balance sheet shows the following:

CAPITAL STOCK AND RETAINED EARNINGS

Preferred stock, $100 par value, 8% cumulative and nonparticipating, issued and outstanding 2,000 shares $200,000	
Common stock, $10 par value, issued and outstanding 25,000 shares 250,000	
Total contributed capital	$450,000
Retained earnings	230,000
Total stockholders' equity	$680,000

1. If there are no dividends in arrears, the book value of the corporation's preferred stock is $_____, and the book value of its common stock is $_____.

2. If a total of two years' dividends are in arrears on the preferred stock, the book value of the preferred stock is $_____, and the book value of the common stock is $_____.

Part V

A corporation accepted subscriptions to 25,000 shares of its $5 par value common stock at $5.50 per share. The subscription contracts called for 20% down payments with the balance in 30 days. The explanations for several entries involving this stock follow. Complete the entries.

DATE		ACCOUNT TITLES AND EXPLANATION	P.R.	DEBIT	CREDIT
Sept.	5				
		Accepted subscriptions to 25,000 shares of common stock at $5.50 per share.			
	5				
		Received $27,500 from the common stock subscribers as down payments on their shares.			
Oct.	5				
		Received payment in full of the balance due on the September 5 common stock subscriptions.			
	5				
		Issued the common stock of the fully paid subscribers			

Part VI

Vector Corporation has outstanding 3,000 shares of $100 par value, 7% cumulative and nonparticipating preferred stock and 10,000 shares of $10 par value common stock. Dividends have not been paid on the preferred stock for the current and one prior year. The corporation has recently prospered, and the board of directors has voted to pay out $49,000 of the corporation's retained earnings in dividends.

1. If the $49,000 is paid out, the preferred stockholders should receive $ _____ per share and the common stockholders should receive $_____ per share.

2. If the foregoing preferred stock were noncumulative rather than cumulative, the preferred stockholders should receive $_____ per share and the common stockholders should receive $_____ per share.

Part I

Book value of a share of stock	15	Organization costs	12
Common stock	2	Participating preferred stock	13
Common stock subscribed	5	Par value	11
Cumulative preferred stock	9	Preemptive right	7
Discount on stock	20	Preferred stock	18
Dividend	16	Premium on stock	14
Dividends in arrears	3	Proxy	4
Minimum legal capital	17	Redemption value of stock	19
Noncumulative preferred stock	6	Stated value of no-par stock	10
No-par stock	8	Stock subscription	1

Part II

1. (X)	5. (O)	9. (X)	13. (X)	17. (X)
2. (X)	6. (O)	10. (X)	14. (O)	18. (X)
3. (O)	7. (X)	11. (O)	15. (X)	
4. (X)	8. (X)	12. (O)	16. (O)	

Part III

1. intangible, five

2. corporation creditors, minimum legal capital

3. par value

4. premium

5. (a) discount liability, (b) par value

6. corporation creditors

7. the payment of dividends, in the distribution of assets if the corporation is liquidated

8. minimum legal capital

9. lack of stockholder liability, ease of transferring ownership rights, continuity of life, no mutual agency, and ease of capital assembly

10. an individual body, separate and distinct from its stockholders

11. nothing

Part IV

1. $100, $19.20
2. $116, $17.92

Part V

Sept. 5	Subscriptions Receivable, Common Stock	137,500.00		
	Common Stock Subscribed		125,000.00	
	Premium on Common Stock		12,500.00	
5	Cash	27,500.00		
	Subscriptions Receivable, Common Stock		27,500.00	
Oct. 5	Cash	110,000.00		
	Subscriptions Receivable, Common Stock		110,000.00	
5	Common Stock Subscribed	125,000.00		
	Common Stock		125,000.00	

Part VI

1. $14, $0.70
2. $ 7, $2.80

16

Additional Corporation Transactions and Stock Investments

Your objectives in studying this chapter should include learning how to:

Record stock dividends and compare them with stock splits.

Record purchases and sales of treasury stock and describe their effects on stockholders' equity.

Describe restrictions and appropriations of retained earnings and the disclosure of such items in the financial statements.

State the criteria for classifying stock investments as current assets or as long-term investments.

Describe the circumstances under which the cost method of accounting for stock investments is used and the circumstances under which the equity method is used.

Record and maintain the accounts for stock investments according to the cost method and the equity method.

Prepare consolidated financial statements that include such matters as excess of investment cost over book value and minority interests.

Define or explain the words and phrases listed in the chapter Glossary.

Topical Outline

I. Dividends, retained earnings, and contributed capital

   A. Cash dividend—reduces in equal amounts both cash and stockholders' equity. In order to pay a cash dividend:

     1. A corporation (in most states) must have retained earnings, and
     2. A corporation must also have sufficient cash.

   B. Generally, contributed capital may not be returned to stockholders as dividends. However, in some states, dividends may be debited or charged to certain contributed capital accounts.

   C. Stock dividend—a distribution of a corporation's own stock to its stockholders without any consideration being received in return from the stockholders.

     1. Small stock dividend—up to 25 percent of the previously outstanding shares; the market value of the shares to be distributed is capitalized.
     2. Large stock dividend—over 25 percent of the previously outstanding shares; only the legally required minimum amount of retained earnings must be capitalized.
     3. When common stock dividends are declared, the par amount is credited to a contributed capital account (Common Stock Dividends Distributable) and any premium is also recorded. The par amount is transferred to Common Stock when the shares are distributed.

II. Stock splits—involve calling in the outstanding shares of stock and replacing them with a larger number of shares which have a lower par value.

   A. Usual purpose is to reduce the market price of the stock to facilitate trading in the stock.
   B. In recording a stock split only a memorandum entry is required.
   C. The total par value of outstanding shares does not change, and retained earnings is not capitalized.

III. Treasury stock—a corporation's own stock that has been issued and then reacquired.

   A. When a corporation purchases its own stock, it reduces in equal amounts both its assets and its stockholders' equity.
   B. Retained earnings equal to the cost of treasury stock are restricted.
   C. Reissuing treasury stock

     1. When sold above cost, the amount received in excess of cost is credited to Contributed Capital, Treasury Stock Transactions.
     2. When sold below cost, the "loss" is debited to Retained Earnings unless there is a contributed capital account from treasury stock transactions, in which case, the "loss" is debited to that account.

   D. Retirement of stock

     1. When stock is purchased for retirement, all capital items related to the shares being retired are removed from the accounts.
     2. A "gain" on the transaction should be credited to contributed capital.
     3. A "loss" on the transaction should be debited to Retained Earnings.

IV. Stocks as investments

   A. Classifying investments

     1. Marketable equity securities—stocks that are marketable and held as investments of cash available for current operations are listed as current assets.
     2. Long-term investments—stocks that are not marketable or not intended to serve as ready sources of cash are classified as noncurrent assets.

B. Accounting for investments in stock

    1. Cost method—used when the investor does not have a significant influence over the investee. The investor usually owns less than 20 percent of the investee's voting stock.

        a. Investor records entire cost of stock as a debit to the investment account.
        b. Each portfolio of stock (current or noncurrent) must be reported at the lower of cost or market.

    2. Equity method—used when the investor has a significant influence (usually owns 20 percent or more of the voting stock of another corporation).

        a. Investor records purchase at cost (as under the cost method).
        b. The investor corporation's share of the investee corporation's earnings is reported as an increase in the Investment account and as Earnings from Investment.

V. Parent and subsidiary corporations

A. Consolidated financial statements—prepared when one corporation (parent) controls another corporation (subsidiary). The parent must own more than 50 percent of the subsidiary's voting stock.

    1. A work sheet is used to effect the consolidation.
    2. Duplication in items is eliminated so that they are not counted twice (e.g., parent's Investment in Subsidiary and subsidiary's equity accounts).
    3. Minority interest—the portion of the subsidiary that is not owned by the parent.
    4. Excess of investment cost over book value—created when parent pays more than book value for its share of the subsidiary. This excess should be allocated to subsidiary's assets and liabilities so that they are restated at fair values. Any remaining excess is reported as "Goodwill from consolidation."

Part I

Many of the important ideas and concepts discussed in Chapter 16 are reflected in the following list of key terms. Test your understanding of these terms by matching the appropriate definitions with the terms. Record the number identifying the most appropriate definition in the blank space next to each term.

_____ Appropriated retained earnings   _____ Minority interest

_____ Consolidated statements   _____ Parent company

_____ Cost method of accounting for stock investments   _____ Restricted retained earnings

_____ Small stock dividend

_____ Earned surplus   _____ Stock dividend

_____ Equity method of accounting for stock investments   _____ Stock split

_____ Subsidiary

_____ Long-term investments   _____ Treasury stock

_____ Marketable equity securities

1. Financial statements that show the results of all operations under the parent's control, including those of any subsidiaries. Assets and liabilities of all affiliated companies are combined on a single balance sheet and their revenues and expenses are combined on a single income statement as though the business were in fact a single company.

2. Investments not intended as a ready source of cash in case of need, such as bond sinking funds, land, and marketable securities that are not held as a temporary investment of cash available for current operations.

3. A corporation that owns a controlling interest (more than 50 percent of the voting stock is required) in another corporation.

4. A distribution by a corporation of shares of its own common stock to its common stockholders without any consideration being received in return.

5. The portion of a subsidiary corporation's stockholders' equity that is not owned by the parent corporation.

6. An accounting method whereby the investment is recorded at total cost and maintained at that amount; subsequent investee earnings and dividends do not affect the investment account.

7. An accounting method whereby the investment is recorded at total cost and the investment account balance is subsequently increased to reflect the investor's equity in earnings of the investee, and decreased to reflect the investor's equity in dividends of the investee.

8. The act of a corporation of calling in its stock and issuing more than one new share in the place of each share previously outstanding.

9. Issued stock that has been reacquired by the issuing corporation.

10. Retained earnings that are unavailable for dividends as a result of law or binding contract.

11. Common and preferred stocks that are actively traded so that sales prices or bid and ask prices are currently available on a national securities exchange or in the over-the-counter market.

12. A synonym for retained earnings, no longer in general use.

13. Retained earnings voluntarily earmarked for a special use as a means of informing stockholders that assets from earnings equal to the appropriations are unavailable for dividends.

14. A corporation that is controlled by another (parent) corporation because the parent owns more than 50 percent of the subsidiary's voting stock.

15. A stock dividend amounting to 25 percent or less of the issuing corporation's previously outstanding shares.

Part II

Complete the following by filling in the blanks.

1. Retained earnings are that part of _____

   _____ that has arisen from retaining in the

   business assets from _____.

2. A stock split _____ (does, does not) have any effect on total stockholders' equity, the equities of the individual stockholders, or on the balances of any of the corporation's contributed capital or retained earnings accounts.

3. If a corporation acquired _____ of another corporation's common stock, the investor is presumed to have a significant influence on the investee corporation's operations, and the investment should be accounted for

   according to the _____.

4. When a corporation purchases treasury stock, a portion of its retained earnings equal to the

   cost of the treasury stock becomes _____ and unavailable

   for _____.

5. If treasury stock is reissued at a price above cost, the amount received in excess of cost is

   credited to _____

   _____. If treasury stock is sold below cost the

   difference between cost and the sale price is debited to either _____

   _____

   or _____.

6. When a company pays more than book value for another company, it indicates that the

   acquired company's assets are _____ or that its

   liabilities are _____ or that the acquired company's earnings prospects are favorable enough to justify paying more than the sum of the fair (market) values of its assets and liabilities.

7. In most jurisdictions a corporation may purchase treasury stock only to the extent of its

   _____ available for dividends.

8. A stock dividend enables a corporation to give its shareholders some evidence of their

   interest in its retained earnings without reducing corporation _____

   _____ or other assets.

9. Treasury stock is a corporation's own stock that has been issued and _____

   _____ either through gift or purchase.

10. Some stockholders may like to receive _____ because many corporations maintain a policy of paying the same cash dividend per share regardless of an increase in the number of shares outstanding.

11. The appropriation of retained earnings _____ (does, does not) set aside cash or funds for a special purpose.

12. The fact that a corporation has a large balance of retained earnings does not necessarily mean that it can pay a cash dividend because _____
_____.

13. A cash dividend reduces a corporation's cash and its stockholders' equity, but a stock dividend does not affect either _____ or total _____
_____.

14. Retained earnings are appropriated or "earmarked" as a means of informing the stockholders that _____
_____.

15. Treasury stock differs from unissued stock in that treasury stock may be reissued at a discount without _____
_____.

Part III

On August 10 Mainline Corporation purchased for cash 2,000 shares of its own $25 par value common stock at $27 per share. On October 3 it sold 1,000 of the shares at $30 per share. Complete the entries below to record the purchase and sale of the stock.

DATE		ACCOUNT TITLES AND EXPLANATION	P.R.	DEBIT	CREDIT
Aug.	10				
		Purchased 2,000 shares of treasury stock.			
Oct.	3				
		Sold 1,000 shares of treasury stock.			

31

Part IV

On December 15, 19—, the board of directors of a corporation appropriated $50,000 of the balance of the corporation's Retained Earnings account as an addition to its retained earnings appropriated for factory expansion. The appropriation was the last of ten such appropriations and brought the balance of the Retained Earnings Appropriated for Factory Expansion account to $500,000. On the following July 10 a contractor completed the factory addition for which the retained earnings were appropriated and was paid $205,400, the contract price for his work. At their meeting on the following August 24 the board of directors voted to return the balance of the Retained Earnings Appropriated for Factory Expansion account to the Retained Earnings account and to distribute a stock dividend in which the par value of the common stock distributed would equal the amount returned. On that date the market value of the stock approximately equaled its par value. The stock dividend was distributed on September 25.

The explanations for the journal entries to record the foregoing series of transactions follow. Complete the entries.

DATE		ACCOUNT TITLES AND EXPLANATION	P.R.	DEBIT	CREDIT
19— Dec.	15				
		Appropriated $50,000 of retained earnings.			
July	10				
		Paid the contract price of the plant addition.			
Aug.	24				
		Returned the balance of retained earnings			
		appropriated for plant expansion to unappropriated			
		retained earnings.			
	24				
		Declared a stock dividend.			

32

Part IV (concluded)

DATE		ACCOUNT TITLES AND EXPLANATION	P.R.	DEBIT	CREDIT
Sept.	25				
		Distributed the stock dividend declared on August 24.			

Part V

The May 31 balance sheet of Eastwood Corporation carried the following stockholders' equity section:

Stockholders' Equity

Common stock, $10 par value, 25,000 shares authorized, 20,000 shares
  issued $200,000
Retained earnings 44,000
Total contributed and retained capital $244,000

On the balance sheet date, with the common stock selling at $12 per share, the corporation's board of directors voted a 2,000-share stock dividend distributable on June 30 to the June 20 stockholders of record.

1. In the space below give without explanations the entries to record the declaration and distribution of the dividend.

DATE		ACCOUNT TITLES AND EXPLANATION	P.R.	DEBIT	CREDIT

Part V (concluded)

2. Harold Jax owned 2,000 shares of the corporation's common stock before the declaration and distribution of the stock dividend; as a result, his portion of the dividend was _____ _____ shares. The total book value of Jax's 2,000 shares before the dividend was $_____; the total book value of his shares after the dividend was $_____; consequently, Jax gained $_____ in the book value of his interest in the corporation.

Part VI

On January 1, 198A, Large Company paid $90,000 for 36,000 of Small Company's 60,000 outstanding common shares. Small Company paid a dividend of $20,000 on November 1, 198A, and at the end of the year reported earnings of $40,000. On January 3, 198B, Large Company sold its interest in Small Company for $120,000.

1. What method should be used to account for Large Company's investment?

_____

2. Complete general journal entries for Large Company to record the facts presented above. Do not give explanations and skip a line between entries.

DATE	ACCOUNT TITLES AND EXPLANATION	P.R.	DEBIT	CREDIT

Part VII

Complete the working paper below under the assumption that Parent Company paid $95,000 for 90% of the outstanding stock of Subsidiary Company, after which it lent its subsidiary $20,000, taking a promissory note as evidence of the debt.

PARENT COMPANY AND SUBSIDIARY COMPANY
Work Sheet for Consolidated Balance Sheet
As of Date of Consolidation

	PARENT COMPANY	SUBSIDIARY COMPANY	ELIMINATIONS DR.	ELIMINATIONS CR.	CONSOLIDATED AMOUNTS
Assets					
Cash	5 0 0 0 00	2 0 0 0 0 00			
Note receivable	2 0 0 0 0 00				
Investment in					
Subsidiary Co.	9 5 0 0 0 00				
Plant and equipment	9 0 0 0 0 00	7 3 0 0 0 00			
Excess of cost over					
book value					
	21 0 0 0 0 00	9 3 0 0 0 00			
Liabilities and Equities					
Accounts payable	8 0 0 0 00	3 0 0 0 00			
Note payable		2 0 0 0 0 00			
Common stock	12 0 0 0 0 00	5 0 0 0 0 00			
Retained earnings	8 2 0 0 0 00	2 0 0 0 0 00			
Minority interest					
	21 0 0 0 0 00	9 3 0 0 0 00			

35

Part I

Part II

1. stockholders' equity, earnings
2. does not
3. 20% or more, equity method
4. restricted, dividends
5. Contributed Capital, Treasury Stock Transactions; Contributed Capital, Treasury Stock Transactions; Retained Earnings
6. undervalued, overvalued
7. retained earnings
8. cash
9. reacquired
10. stock dividends
11. does not
12. it may not have sufficient cash
13. cash, stockholders' equity
14. assets equal in amount to the appropriation will not be paid out in dividends
15. discount liability

Part III

Aug. 10	Treasury Stock, Common	54,000.00	
	Cash		54,000.00
Oct. 3	Cash	30,000.00	
	Treasury Stock, Common		27,000.00
	Contributed Capital, Treasury Stock Transactions		3,000.00

Part IV

Dec. 15	Retained Earnings	50,000.00	
	Retained Earnings Appropriated for Factory Expansion		50,000.00
July 10	Buildings	205,400.00	
	Cash		205,400.00
Aug. 24	Retained Earnings Appropriated for Factory Expansion	500,000.00	
	Retained Earnings		500,000.00
24	Retained Earnings	500,000.00	
	Common Stock Dividend Distributable		500,000.00
Sept. 25	Common Stock Dividend Distributable	500,000.00	
	Common Stock		500,000.00

Part V

1. May 31	Retained Earnings	24,000.00	
	Common Stock Dividend Distributable		20,000.00
	Contributed Capital in Excess of Par Value, Common Stock		4,000.00
June 30	Common Stock Dividend Distributable	20,000.00	
	Common Stock		20,000.00

2. 200 shares, $24,400, $24,400, $0

Part VI

1. The equity method

2. 198A

Jan. 1	Investment in Small Company	90,000.00	
	Cash		90,000.00
Nov. 1	Cash	12,000.00	
	Investment in Small Company		12,000.00
Dec. 31	Investment in Small Company	24,000.00	
	Earnings from Investment in Small Company ..		24,000.00

198B

Jan. 3	Cash	120,000.00	
	Investment in Small Company		102,000.00
	Gain on Sale of Investments		18,000.00

Part VII

PARENT COMPANY AND SUBSIDIARY COMPANY
Work Sheet for Consolidated Balance Sheets
As of Date of Consolidation

	Parent Company	Subsidiary Company	Eliminations		Consolidated Amounts
			Dr.	Cr.	
Assets					
Cash	5,000	20,000	....	....	25,000
Note receivable	20,000	.....	....	(a) 20,000	....
Investment in Subsidiary Co.	95,000	.....	....	(b) 95,000	....
Plant and equipment	90,000	73,000	....	....	163,000
Excess of cost over book value	....	.....	(b) 32,000	....	32,000
	210,000	93,000			220,000
Liabilities and Equities					
Accounts payable	8,000	3,000	....	....	11,000
Note payable	....	20,000	(a) 20,000	....	....
Common stock	120,000	50,000	(b) 50,000	....	120,000
Retained earnings	82,000	20,000	(b) 20,000	....	82,000
Minority interest	....	.....	....	(b) 7,000	7,000
	210,000	93,000	122,000	122,000	220,000

17

Installment Notes Payable and Bonds

Your objectives in studying this chapter should include learning how to:

Calculate and record the payments on an installment note.

Explain the differences between an installment note payable, a bond, and a share of stock.

Describe the advantages and disadvantages of securing capital by issuing bonds.

Explain how bond interest rates are established.

Use present value tables to calculate the premium or the discount on a bond issue.

Prepare entries to account for bonds issued between interest dates at par.

Prepare entries to account for bonds sold at par, at a discount, or at a premium.

Explain the purpose and operation of a bond sinking fund and prepare entries for its operation.

Describe the procedures used to account for investments in bonds.

Define or explain the words and phrases listed in the chapter Glossary.

Topical Outline

I. Installment notes payable

    A. Borrower pays back debt by making a series of periodic payments, either in the form of:

        1. Equal payments, where interest and principal amounts vary, and total amount of payment stays the same, or

        2. Payments that vary in total amount and consist of accrued interest to date plus equal amounts of principal.

    B. Difference between notes payable and bonds

        1. Usually a single creditor (e.g., a bank) is involved when a business or individual borrows by signing a note payable.

        2. A bond issue generally includes a large number of bonds sold to many different lenders. Bonds may be owned by a number of people before they mature.

II. Bonds

    A. Difference between stocks and bonds

        1. A share of stock represents an equity or ownership right in a corporation. (Stockholders are owners.)

        2. A bond represents a debt or liability of the corporation issuing the bond. (Bondholders are creditors.)

    B. Reasons for issuing bonds

        1. Issuance of bonds instead of stock often results in increased earnings for common stockholders.

        2. Bond interest must be paid whether or not there are earnings, but interest payments are expenses and are tax-deductible.

    C. Rights of bondholders

        1. To receive periodic interest payments.

        2. To receive the face value of the bond when it matures.

    D. Types of bonds

        1. Serial bonds—an issue of bonds with varying maturity dates, so that the entire bond issue is repaid in installments over a period of years.

        2. Sinking fund bonds—paid at maturity from a special fund created for that purpose.

        3. Registered bonds—ownership is recorded with the issuing corporation.

        4. Coupon bonds—have interest coupons that must be presented to receive interest payments.

        5. Debentures—unsecured bonds.

    E. Issuing bonds

        1. Issuing corporation sells bonds to an investment firm (the underwriter), which resells bonds to the public.

        2. Bond indenture—written, legal document that states the rights and obligations of the issuing company and the bondholders.

        3. A trustee (usually a bank or trust company) oversees the fulfillment of contract obligation to the bondholders.

        4. Contract rate of bond interest—rate of interest applied to the par value (face amount) of bonds to determine annual cash payment to bondholders.

        5. Market rate of bond interest—interest rate that a corporation is willing to pay and investors are willing to take for use of their money to buy that corporation's bonds.

a. Bond discount—the bond will sell for an amount less than face value if the market rate of bond interest is greater than the contract rate of bond interest.

b. Bond premium—the bond will sell for an amount greater than face value if the market rate of bond interest is less than the contract rate of bond interest.

6. Bonds sold between interest dates—interest that has accrued on the bonds since the previous interest payment date is customarily charged and collected from purchasers.

F. Accounting for bonds after issuance

1. Bond discount or bond premium must be amortized.

a. Straight-line method—equal portion of the discount or premium amortized each period.

b. Interest method—amount of discount or premium amortized changes each period.

2. End-of-accounting-period adjustments for accrued interest must be made.

G. Additional features of bonds

1. Callable bonds—may be redeemed at the issuing corporation's option, usually upon the payment of a redemption premium. (Not all bonds have this provision.)

2. Bond sinking fund—to provide investors with greater security, a corporation may agree to make periodic cash deposits with a sinking fund trustee. Fund is used to pay bondholders when the bonds become due.

3. Convertible bonds—may be exchanged for shares of issuing corporation's stock at option of bondholders.

H. Investments in bonds

1. Purchasers of bonds may not hold them to maturity, but may sell them to other investors.

2. Purchasers record bonds at cost, including any brokerage fees.

3. Any discount or premium on bonds held as long-term investments should be amortized using procedures similar to those for bonds payable.

4. A bond investment is shown as a current asset at cost (with no discount or premium amortization) only if the bonds are held as short-term, temporary investments.

III. Mortgages

A. Bonds or notes payable are either secured or unsecured.

B. Many notes payable and bond issues are secured by a mortgage.

C. Mortgage—the legal agreement that helps protect a lender by giving the lender the right to be paid from the cash proceeds from the sale of the borrower's mortgaged assets, if the borrower fails to make payments required by a note payable or bond indenture.

D. Terms of mortgage are written in a separate legal document—a mortgage contract—which normally grants the lender (the mortgage holder) the right to foreclose if the borrower fails to pay.

Part I

Many of the important ideas and concepts discussed in Chapter 17 are reflected in the following list of key terms. Test your understanding of these terms by matching the appropriate definitions with the terms. Record the number identifying the most appropriate definition in the blank space next to each term.

_____	Bearer bond	_____	Debenture
_____	Bond	_____	Face amount of a bond
_____	Bond discount	_____	Installment notes
_____	Bond indenture	_____	Market rate for bond interest
_____	Bond premium	_____	Mortgage
_____	Bond sinking fund	_____	Mortgage contract
_____	Callable bond	_____	Par value of a bond
_____	Carrying amount of a bond issue	_____	Registered bond
_____	Contract rate of bond interest	_____	Serial bonds
_____	Convertible bond	_____	Sinking fund bonds
_____	Coupon bond		

1. The contract between the issuing corporation and the bondholders that states the rights and obligations of both parties.

2. The difference between the par value of a bond and the price at which it is issued when issued at a price below par.

3. The interest rate that a corporation is willing to pay and investors are willing to take for the use of their money to buy that corporation's bonds.

4. A fund of assets accumulated to repay a bond issue at maturity.

5. A legal document setting forth the rights of the lender and the obligations of the borrower with respect to mortgaged assets.

6. A bond that is not registered and is made payable to whoever holds the bond (the bearer).

7. The par value of a bond issue less any unamortized discount or plus any unamortized premium.

8. A legal agreement that helps protect a lender by giving the lender the right to be paid from the cash proceeds from the sale of the borrower's mortgaged assets.

9. The difference between the par value of a bond and the price at which it is issued when issued at a price above par.

10. Bonds that require the issuing corporation to accumulate a separate fund of assets during the life of the bonds for the purpose of repaying the bondholders at maturity.

11. A bond that has interest coupons attached to the bond certificate, which are detached and submitted to the issuing corporation for payment.

12. An issue of bonds that mature at different points in time so that the entire bond issue is repaid gradually over a period of years.

13. A bond that may be redeemed or repaid before its maturity date at the option of the issuing corporation.

14. The rate of interest that is applied to the par value of bonds to determine the annual cash payment to the bondholders.

15. The face amount of the bond, which is the amount the borrower agrees to repay at maturity and the amount on which interest payments are based.

16. An unsecured bond.

17. The bond's par value.

18. A bond that may be exchanged for shares of its issuing corporation's stock at the option of the bondholder.

19. Notes that require a series of payments consisting of interest plus a portion of the original amount borrowed.

20. A bond for which the name and address of the owners are recorded.

21. A long-term liability of a corporation or governmental unit, usually issued in denominations of $1,000, and requiring periodic payments of interest and final payment of par value when it matures.

Part II

Complete the following by filling in the blanks.

1. A bond sinking fund offers a measure of security to bondholders, since it is a fund of assets accumulated to _____ the bondholders at maturity.

2. Two important rights given to the owner of a bond are:

   a) _____
   _____, and

   b) _____
   _____.

3. A bond sinking fund would normally be shown in the section of the balance sheet entitled
   _____.

4. Often a corporation cannot obtain debt financing without providing security to the creditors by the issuance of a _____.

5. When a corporation sells bonds between interest dates, it collects accrued interest from the purchasers. As a result the corporation does not have to keep a record of the purchasers and the _____ on which they bought bonds, for it can pay a full period's interest to all purchasers for the period in which they bought bonds, and every purchaser receives the amount of interest he has _____ and gets back the accrued interest paid at the time of purchase.

6. When bonds are purchased as a temporary investment, the bond investment appears on the balance sheet as a _____.

7. The rate of interest a corporation agrees to pay on a bond issue is called the _____ rate. This rate is applied to the _____ value of the bonds to determine the amount of interest that must be paid.

8. In the interest of the bondholders and as protection for the issuing corporation's financial position, a _____ may restrict the dividends a corporation may pay while its bonds are outstanding.

9. A disadvantage of securing capital through the sale of bonds is that the bondholders are _____ and must be paid whether or not there are earnings.

44

10. Bonds that may be exchanged for shares of the issuing company's common stock are called _____ bonds.

11. If a corporation offers to sell a bond issue on which the contract rate of interest is below the market rate, the bonds will sell at a _____; and if it offers to sell bonds on which the contract rate is above the market rate, the bonds will sell at a _____.

12. A $1,000 bond with a contract rate of bond interest of 9 percent would provide semiannual interest payments of $_____.

13. Bonds that may be redeemed at the issuing company's option are known as _____ bonds.

14. An advantage of securing capital through the sale of bonds as opposed to securing it through the sale of stock is that bondholders do not share in either _____ or _____.

15. The accounting procedure for dividing a discount and charging a fair share to each period in the life of the applicable bond issue is called _____ _____.

16. The terms of installment notes payable require one of two payment plans:

a) _____
   _____, or

b) _____
   _____.

Part III

On May 1, 198B, JJR Corporation purchased 125 $1,000, 9%, ten-year bonds dated December 31, 198A, at a price of 95 plus a $500 brokerage fee, from LLB Co. as a short-term investment.

Make the journal entries to record the purchase of the bonds and to record the receipt of interest on June 30, 198B (assuming interest is paid semiannually on June 30 and December 31).

DATE		ACCOUNT TITLES AND EXPLANATION	P.R.	DEBIT	CREDIT
198B May	1				
		Purchased 125 $1,000, 9%, ten-year bonds dated December 31, 198A, at a price of 95 plus a $500 brokerage fee and accrued interest.			
June	30				
		To record receipt of interest on bonds purchased May 1 from LLB Co.			

Part IV

On December 15, 1985, Candida Corporation deposited a bond indenture with the trustee of its bondholders authorizing it to issue $1,000,000 of 10.2%, 20-year bonds, dated January 1, 1986, and upon which interest is payable each June 30 and December 31. The bonds were issued at par plus accrued interest on February 1, 1986.

1. Complete the 1986 entries for this bond issue.

DATE		ACCOUNT TITLES AND EXPLANATION	P.R.	DEBIT	CREDIT
1986 Feb.	1				
		Sold $1,000,000 of 10.2%, 20-year bonds at par plus one month's accrued interest.			
June	30				
		Paid the semiannual interest on the bonds.			
Dec.	31				
		Paid the semiannual interest on the bonds.			

2. Post to the T-account below the portions of the above entries that affect bond interest expense and then complete the statement that follows.

Bond Interest Expense

Candida Corporation's 1986 income statement should show $_____ of bond interest expense and its 1987 income statement should show $_____ of bond interest expense.

47

Part V

On January 1, 1985, a day on which the market rate for bond interest was 10 percent, Bullock Company sold bonds having a $100,000 par value, a five-year life, and on which interest was to be paid semiannually at a 9 percent annual rate.

1. The buyer of these bonds received two rights: (a) the right to receive $_____ _____ in interest at the end of each six-month interest period throughout the five-year life of the bond issue, and (b) the right to receive $_____ at the end of the bond issue's life.

2. To determine the present value of the rights received and to determine the price to pay for the rights, the buyer of the bonds should discount the rights at the _____% market rate for bond interest prevailing on the day of the purchase.

3. The calculations for determining the percent value of the bond buyer's two rights, using the tables in Chapter 12 in the text are:

    Present value of $100,000 to be received _____ periods

    hence, discounted at _____% per period ($100,000 ×

    _____) .... $_____

    Present value of $_____ to be received periodically

    for _____ periods, discounted at _____%

    ($_____ × _____) .... _____

    Price to pay for the bonds .... $_____

4. Bullock Corporation's entry to record the sale of the bonds at their present value is:

DATE		ACCOUNT TITLES AND EXPLANATION	P.R.	DEBIT	CREDIT
1985 Jan.	1				
		Sold bonds at a discount.			

5. At the end of the first semiannual interest period Bullock Corporation calculated the number of dollars of interest to be paid its bondholders as follows:

$\underline{\hspace{3cm}} \times \underline{\hspace{1.5cm}}\% = \$\underline{\hspace{3cm}}$

6. The company then began its calculation of the amount of interest expense to be recorded for the first semiannual interest period and the amount of discount to be amortized by first determining the beginning-of-the-period carrying amount for the bonds with this calculation:

$\underline{\hspace{3cm}} - \$\underline{\hspace{3cm}} = \$\underline{\hspace{3cm}}$

7. Using the interest method, the company then calculated the amount of interest expense to be recorded at the end of the first semiannual interest period as follows:

$\underline{\hspace{3cm}} \times \underline{\hspace{1.5cm}}\% = \$\underline{\hspace{3cm}}$

8. Next, the company determined the amount of discount to be amortized with this calculation:

$\underline{\hspace{3cm}} - \$\underline{\hspace{3cm}} = \$\underline{\hspace{3cm}}$

9. After making these calculations, Bullock Corporation recorded the interest paid its bondholders and the discount amortized with this entry:

DATE		ACCOUNT TITLES AND EXPLANATION	P.R.	DEBIT	CREDIT
1985 June	30				
		Paid the semiannual interest on the bonds and			
		amortized a portion of the discount.			

Part VI

On December 31, 198A, HX Company borrowed $60,000 by signing a 14% installment note that is to be repaid with six annual payments, the first of which is due on December 31, 198B.

a) Prepare a general journal entry to record the borrowing of the money.

DATE	ACCOUNT TITLES AND EXPLANATION	P.R.	DEBIT	CREDIT

b) Assume that the payments are to consist of accrued interest plus equal amounts of principal. Prepare general journal entries to record the first and second installment payments.

DATE	ACCOUNT TITLES AND EXPLANATION	P.R.	DEBIT	CREDIT

c) Contrary to the assumption in (b) above, assume now that the note requires each installment payment to be $15,464. Prepare general journal entries to record the first and second installment payments. (Round all amounts to the nearest whole dollar.)

DATE	ACCOUNT TITLES AND EXPLANATION	P.R.	DEBIT	CREDIT

Solutions for Chapter 17

Part I

Part II

1. repay

2. a) the right to receive periodic interest payments
   b) the right to receive the face amount of the bond when it matures

3. long-term investments

4. mortgage

5. dates, earned

6. current asset

7. contract, par

8. bond indenture

9. creditors

10. convertible

11. discount; premium

12. $45

13. callable

14. management, earnings

15. amortizing a discount

16. a) payments of accrued interest plus equal amounts of principal
    b) payments that are equal in total amount, consisting of changing amounts of interest and principal

Part III

198B
May 1 Investment in LLB Co. Bonds 119,250.00
        Bond Interest Receivable 3,750.00
            Cash 123,000.00

June 30 Cash 5,625.00
            Bond Interest Receivable 3,750.00
            Bond Interest Earned 1,875.00

Part IV

1.
Feb. 1 Cash 1,008,500.00
            Bond Interest Expense 8,500.00
            Bonds Payable 1,000,000.00

June 30 Bond Interest Expense 51,000.00
            Cash 51,000.00

Dec. 31 Bond Interest Expense 51,000.00
            Cash 51,000.00

2.
	Bond Interest Expense		
June 30	51,000.00	Feb. 1	8,500.00
Dec. 31	51,000.00		

$93,500, $102,000

Part V

1. (a) $4,500, (b) $100,000

2. 10

3. Present value of $100,000 to be received 10 periods hence, discounted at 5% per
        period ($100,000 × .6139) $61,390
    Present value of $4,500 to be received periodically for 10 periods, discounted at
        5% ($4,500 × 7.7217) 34,748*
    Price to pay for the bonds $96,138*

        *rounded to the nearest whole dollar

4. Jan. 1 Cash 96,138.00
            Discount on Bonds Payable 3,862.00
                Bonds Payable 100,000.00

5. $100,000 × 0.045 = $4,500

6. $100,000 − $3,862 = $96,138

7. $96,138 × 0.05 = $4,807 (rounded to the nearest whole dollar)

8. $4,807 − $4,500 = $307

9. June 30 Bond Interest Expense 4,807.00
                Discount on Bonds Payable 307.00
                Cash 4,500.00

Part VI

a) 198A
   Dec. 31 Cash 60,000.00
                Notes Payable 60,000.00

b) 198B
   Dec. 31 Interest Expense ($60,000 × .14) 8,400.00
            Notes Payable 10,000.00
                Cash 18,400.00

   198C
   Dec. 31 Interest Expense ($50,000 × .14) 7,000.00
            Notes Payable 10,000.00
                Cash 17,000.00

c) 198B
   Dec. 31 Interest Expense ($60,000 × .14) 8,400.00
            Notes Payable 7,064.00
                Cash 15,464.00

   198C
   Dec. 31 Interest Expense ($60,000 − $7,064) × .14 .... 7,411.00
            Notes Payable 8,053.00
                Cash ....

18

Statement of Changes in Financial Position

Your objectives in studying this chapter should include learning how to:

List the items included in working capital and explain why an adequate amount of working capital is important in the operation of a business.

List a number of sources and uses of working capital.

Explain why the net income reported on an income statement is not the amount of working capital generated by operations.

Describe the adjustments that must be made to the reported net income figure in order to determine the amount of working capital generated by operations.

Prepare a statement of changes in financial position on a working capital basis.

Prepare an analysis of changes in working capital items.

Prepare a statement of changes in financial position on a cash basis.

Define or explain the words and phrases listed in the chapter Glossary.

Topical Outline

I. Purpose of statement of changes in financial position

   A. Provides a better understanding of the financing and investing activities of a business.

   B. Summarizes changes that occurred in the financial position of a business by showing:

      1. Where a business acquired resources during the period.

      2. Where a business applied or used resources.

   C. Designed either to:

      1. Emphasize the changes in the working capital of the business, or

      2. Explain changes in cash, or cash plus temporary investments.

   D. Funds

      1. Relatively liquid resources that are or soon will be available to meet the needs of the business; defined as cash, or cash plus temporary investments, or working capital.

      2. Wording in statement of changes should clearly indicate the basis of preparing the statement; that is, cash, cash plus temporary investments, or working capital.

II. Working capital—excess of current assets over current liabilities

   A. An adequate amount of working capital enables a business to meet current debts, carry sufficient inventory, take advantage of cash discounts, and offer favorable credit terms to customers.

   B. Sources of working capital include:

      1. Current operations—net income after adjustments for items that do not affect working capital.

      2. Increases in long-term liabilities.

      3. Sale of noncurrent assets.

      4. Sale of capital stock.

   C. Uses of working capital include:

      1. Purchase of noncurrent assets.

      2. Payment of noncurrent liabilities.

      3. Capital reductions.

      4. Declaration of a dividend that is to be paid in cash or other current assets.

III. Statement of changes in financial position—working capital basis

   A. Prepare an analysis of changes in working capital items (a companion statement to SCFP).

   B. Prepare a working paper to analyze changes in noncurrent accounts.

   C. Use the working paper to prepare a formal statement.

   D. GAAP requires that a SCFP disclose all important aspects of a concern's financing and investing activities even though elements of working capital are not directly affected.

IV. Statement of changes in financial position—cash basis

   A. Prepare a working paper to analyze the changes in all accounts other than cash.

   B. Decide which noncash working capital changes should be added and disclosed as a single item.

   C. Use the working paper to prepare the formal statement.

   D. If SCFP is designed to explain change in cash plus temporary investments, cash and temporary investment balances are added and treated as a single item; other working capital items are listed separately on working paper and analyzed in the same manner as if a cash basis is being used.

Part I

Many of the important ideas and concepts discussed in Chapter 18 are reflected in the following list of key terms. Test your understanding of these terms by matching the appropriate definitions with the terms. Record the number identifying the most appropriate definition in the blank space next to each term.

_____ Funds

_____ Net working capital

_____ Source of working capital

_____ Statement of changes in financial position

_____ Use of working capital

_____ Working capital

1. A transaction that decreases current assets or increases current liabilities.

2. A statement that reports the financing and investing activities of a business during a period, generally indicating their effects on working capital, or cash, or cash plus temporary investments.

3. A synonym for working capital.

4. A transaction that increases current assets or decreases current liabilities.

5. Relatively liquid resources that are or soon will be available to meet the needs of the business; defined as cash, or cash plus temporary investments, or working capital.

6. The excess of a company's current assets over its current liablilities.

Part II

Complete the following by filling in the blanks.

1. Common uses of working capital are _____

   _____

   _____.

2. Common sources of working capital are _____

   _____

   _____.

3. Analyzing entries on a working paper for a statement of changes in financial position _____ (are, are not) entered in the General Journal and posted.

4. The noncurrent accounts of a company are the best source of information for preparing a statement of changes in financial position (working capital basis) because only _____ transactions affect these accounts and almost every such transaction either _____ or _____ working capital.

5. On a statement of changes in financial position (cash basis), the change in working capital (excluding cash and dividends payable) should be shown as _____

   _____.

6. When the statement of changes in financial position is prepared _____

   _____, noncash working capital items must be included among potential sources and uses of cash.

7. The term "funds" may be used to mean:

   a) _____

   b) _____

   c) _____

8. Depreciation _____ (is, is not) a source of funds.

9. A statement of changes in financial position (working capital basis) explains the _____ or _____ in a concern's working capital. This is accomplished by listing on the statement all _____ _____ of new working capital, listing the _____ made of working capital, and then setting out the difference, which is the _____ in working capital.

10. Some examples of expenses that are deducted on the income statement but that do not decrease working capital are:

   a) _____

   b) _____

   c) _____

Below is Flamingo Corporation's unfinished working paper for a statement of changes in financial position and on the next page is its unfinished statement.

FLAMINGO CORPORATION
Working Paper for Statement of Changes in Financial Position
(Working Capital Basis)
For Year Ended December 31, 198B

	ACCOUNT BALANCES 12/31/198A	ANALYZING ENTRIES DEBIT	ANALYZING ENTRIES CREDIT	ACCOUNT BALANCES 12/31/198B
Debits:				
Working capital	45 000 00			49 500 00
Equipment	39 000 00			45 000 00
Totals	84 000 00			94 500 00
Credits:				
Accum. depr., equipment	8 500 00			10 000 00
Mortgage payable	15 000 00			10 500 00
Common stock, $15 par value	40 500 00			45 000 00
Contributed capital in excess of par value, common stock				3 000 00
Retained earnings	20 000 00			26 000 00
Totals	84 000 00			94 500 00
Sources of working capital:				
Current operations:				
Net income				
Depreciation of equipment				
Other sources:				
Sale of stock				
Uses of working capital:				
Purchase of equipment				
Reduction of mortgage				
Declaration of dividends				
Totals				

Required:

1. Use the following information to complete the working paper.

   a. The corporation earned a $14,000 net income in 198B.

   b. It recorded $4,000 of depreciation on its equipment for the year.

   c. Equipment costing $8,500 was purchased in 198B.

   d. Fully depreciated equipment that cost $2,500 was discarded and its cost and accumulated depreciation were removed from the accounts.

   e. The corporation reduced its mortgage with a $4,500 payment.

   f. Three hundred shares of common stock were sold and issued at $25 per share.

   g. Cash dividends totaling $8,000 were declared and paid in 198B.

2. After completing the working paper, use its information to finish the statement of changes in financial position.

FLAMINGO CORPORATION
Statement of Changes in Financial Position
For Year Ended December 31, 198B

Sources of working capital:					
Current operations:					
Net income earned in 198B					
Add expenses not requiring outlays of working capital in					
the current period:					
Depreciation of equipment					
Working capital provided by operations					
Other sources:					
Sale of common stock					
Total new working capital					
Uses of working capital:					
Purchase of equipment					
Reduction of mortgage					
Declaration of dividends					
Total uses of working capital					
Net increase in working capital					

3. Flamingo Corporation's unfinished statement analyzing the changes in working capital items follows. Complete the statement.

FLAMINGO CORPORATION
Analysis of Changes in Working Capital Items
For Year Ended December 31, 198B

	DEC. 31, 198B	DEC. 31, 198A	WORKING CAPITAL INCREASES	WORKING CAPITAL DECREASES
Current assets:				
Cash	10 750 00	6 250 00		
Accounts receivable, net	13 000 00	14 500 00		
Merchandise inventory	49 000 00	51 250 00		
Prepaid expenses	3 250 00	2 500 00		
Total current assets	76 000 00	74 500 00		
Current liabilities:				
Notes payable	4 000 00	3 250 00		
Accounts payable	23 500 00	27 250 00		
Total current liabilities	27 500 00	30 500 00		
Working capital	48 500 00	44 000 00		
Net increase in working capital				

Part IV

Complete the following statements by filling in the blanks.

1. If a statement of changes in financial position is designed to account for the change in cash (instead of for the change in working capital), the statement should show "Sources of _____" and "Uses of _____."

2. When the cash basis is used in preparing the statement of changes in financial position, the _____ items must be included among the potential sources and uses of cash.

3. On a statement of changes in financial position (cash basis), the _____ _____ should be shown as an addition or a subtraction from net income when calculating cash provided by operations.

Solutions for Chapter 18

Part I

Part II

1. purchases of noncurrent assets, payment of noncurrent liabilities, capital reductions, and declaration of dividends

2. current operations, transactions that increase long-term liabilities, sales of noncurrent assets, and sales of capital stock

3. are not

4. a few, increases, decreases

5. an addition to or a subtraction from net income in calculating cash provided by operations

6. on a cash basis

7. a) cash
   b) cash plus temporary investments
   c) working capital

8. is not

9. increase, decrease, sources, uses, net increase or decrease

10. a) depreciation
    b) depletion
    c) bond discount amortization

Part III

1.

FLAMINGO CORPORATION
Working Paper for Statement of Changes in Financial Position
(Working Capital Basis)
For Year Ended December 31, 198B

	Account Balances 12/31/8A	Analyzing Entries Debit	Analyzing Entries Credit	Account Balances 12/31/8B
Debits:				
Working capital	45,000	....	....	49,500
Equipment	39,000	(c) 8,500	(d) 2,500	45,000
Totals	84,000	....	....	94,500
Credits:				
Accum. depr., equipment	8,500	(d) 2,500	(b) 4,000	10,000
Mortgage payable	15,000	(e) 4,500	....	10,500
Common stock, $15 par value	40,500	....	(f) 4,500	45,000
Contributed capital in excess of par value, common stock	....		(f) 3,000	3,000
Retained earnings	20,000	(g) 8,000	(a) 14,000	26,000
Totals	84,000	....	....	94,500
Sources of working capital:				
Current operations:				
Net income	....	(a) 14,000	....	......
Depreciation of equipment	....	(b) 4,000	....	......
Other sources:				
Sale of stock	....	(f) 7,500	....	......
Uses of working capital:				
Purchase of equipment	....	....	(c) 8,500	......
Reduction of mortgage	....	....	(e) 4,500	......
Declaration of dividends	....	....	(g) 8,000	......
Totals	....	49,000	49,000	......

2.
FLAMINGO CORPORATION
Statement of Changes in Financial Position
For Year Ended December 31, 198B

Sources of working capital:
  Current operations:
    Net income earned in 198B $14,000
    Add expenses not requiring outlays of working capital in the current
      period:
      Depreciation of equipment 4,000
    Working capital provided by operations $18,000
  Other sources:
    Sale of common stock 7,500
Total new working capital $25,500
Uses of working capital:
  Purchase of equipment .... $ 8,500
  Reduction of mortgage 4,500
  Declaration of dividends 8,000
  Total uses of working capital 21,000
Net increase in working capital .... $ 4,500

3.
FLAMINGO CORPORATION
Analysis of Changes in Working Capital Items
For Year Ended December 31, 198B

	Dec. 31, 198B	Dec. 31, 198A	Working Capital Increases	Decreases
Current assets:				
Cash	$10,750	$ 6,250	$4,500	....
Accounts receivable, net	13,000	14,500	....	$1,500
Merchandise inventory	49,000	51,250	....	2,250
Prepaid expenses	3,250	2,500	750	....
Total current assets	$76,000	$74,500	....	....
Current liabilities:				
Notes payable	$ 4,000	$ 3,250	....	750
Accounts payable	23,500	27,250	3,750	....
Total current liabilities	$27,500	$30,500	....	....
Working capital	$48,500	$44,000	....	....
			$9,000	$4,500
Net increase in working capital				4,500
			$9,000	$9,000

Part IV

1. cash, cash

2. noncash working capital

3. change in working capital

19

Additional Financial Reporting Issues

Your objectives in studying this chapter should include learning how to:

Describe the income statement sections that follow "Income from continuing operations."

Explain the general requirements for reporting the income effects of a discontinued operation, an extraordinary item, a change in accounting principles, and a prior period adjustment.

State the reasons why conventional financial statements fail to adequately account for price changes.

Explain how price changes should be measured and how to construct a price index.

Restate historical cost/nominal dollar costs into constant dollar amounts and calculate purchasing power gains and losses.

Explain the difference between current costs and historical costs stated in constant dollars.

Describe the FASB requirements for disclosing financial information adjusted for price changes.

Describe the primary problems of accounting for international operations and prepare entries to account for sales to foreign customers.

Define or explain the words and phrases listed in the chapter Glossary.

Topical Outline

I. Income and loss items not directly related to continuing operations

   A. Discontinued operations

      1. Results of operations of a discontinued business segment should be reported in a separate section of the income statement.
      2. Income or loss from operating the segment is separated from the gain or loss on disposal.
      3. Each gain or loss is reported net of related income tax effects.

   B. Extraordinary items

      1. Must be both unusual and infrequent.
      2. Reported (net of related income taxes) below discontinued operations.
      3. Items that are unusual or infrequent (but not both) are reported in the income statement within the category of income from continuing operations.

   C. Changes in accounting principles

      1. Notwithstanding the consistency principle, changes in accounting principles are acceptable if justified as improvements in financial reporting.
      2. Cumulative effect on prior years' incomes is reported (net of taxes) below extraordinary items.

   D. Prior period adjustments

      1. Essentially limited to corrections of errors made in prior periods.
      2. Reported in statement of retained earnings as an adjustment to the beginning retained earnings balance.

II. Accounting for price changes

   A. Conventional financial statements reflect historical costs expressed in nominal dollars.
   B. Price indexes

      1. A price index measures the weighted-average changes in the prices of a particular market basket of goods and/or services.
      2. Specific price indexes measure price changes of a narrow group of products; general price indexes measure price changes of a very broad group of products, or general purchasing power.
      3. General indexes are used to restate dollar amounts of cost paid in one period into dollars with the purchasing power of another period.

   C. Historical cost/constant dollar accounting

      1. Uses a general price index to restate historical cost/nominal dollar statements into historical cost dollar amounts that represent current, general purchasing power.
      2. Procedures involve:

         a. Calculating general purchasing power gain or loss from owning monetary assets or owing monetary liabilities.
         b. Adjusting nonmonetary items for price changes since the items were first purchased.

      3. Does not reflect current values.

D. Current cost accounting

1. Uses specific price indexes and other estimates to report current costs in financial statements.
2. Only nonmonetary items must be adjusted for specific price changes.
3. Certain large companies are required to disclose supplemental current cost information in footnotes to financial statements.
4. Recoverable amounts are reported instead of current costs when the recoverable amounts appear to be materially and permanently lower than current cost.

III. Accounting for international operations

A. Multinational businesses are those having operations in several different countries.
B. Foreign exchange rate—the price of one currency stated in terms of another currency.
C. Sales and purchases denominated in a foreign currency

1. U.S. companies making such sales (or purchases) must translate the transaction amounts into U.S. dollars.
2. Receivables or payables stated in terms of foreign currencies result in exchange gains or losses as the foreign exchange rates fluctuate.

D. Consolidated statements with foreign subsidiaries—prepared using foreign exchange rates to translate the financial statements of the foreign subsidiaries into U.S. dollars.

Part I

Many of the important ideas and concepts discussed in Chapter 19 are reflected in the following list of key terms. Test your understanding of these terms by matching the appropriate definitions with the terms. Record the number identifying the most appropriate definition in the blank space next to each term.

_____	Changes in accounting estimates	_____	Infrequent gain or loss
_____	Current cost	_____	Monetary assets
_____	Current cost accounting	_____	Monetary liabilities
_____	Deflation	_____	Multinational business
_____	Extraordinary gain or loss	_____	Nonmonetary assets
_____	Foreign exchange rate	_____	Nonmonetary liabilities
_____	General price-level index	_____	Price index
_____	General purchasing power gain or loss	_____	Prior period adjustments
		_____	Reporting currency
_____	Historical cost/constant dollar accounting	_____	Segment of a business
		_____	Specific price-level index
_____	Historical cost/nominal dollar financial statements	_____	Unusual gain or loss
_____	Inflation		

1. A gain or loss that is not expected to occur again, given the operating environment of the business.

2. An accounting system that adjusts historical cost/nominal dollar financial statements for changes in the general purchasing power of the dollar.

3. The gain or loss that results from holding monetary assets and/or owing monetary liabilities during a period in which the general price level changes.

4. The price of one currency stated in terms of another currency.

5. Obligations that are not fixed in amount.

6. Fixed amounts that are owed; the number of dollars to be paid does not change regardless of changes in the general price level.

7. Items that are reported in the current statement of retained earnings as corrections to the beginning retained earnings balance; limited primarily to corrections of errors made in past years.

8. Assets that have fluctuating prices.

9. A company that operates in a large number of different countries.

10. A gain or loss that is both unusual and infrequent of occurrence.

11. A measure of the changes in prices of a particular market basket of goods and/or services.

12. An accounting system that uses specific price-level indexes (and other means) to develop financial statements that report items such as assets and expenses in terms of the current costs to acquire or replace those assets or services.

13. The currency in which a company presents its financial statements.

14. A general increase in the prices paid for goods and services.

15. In general, the cost that would be required to acquire (or replace) an asset or service at the present time. On the income statement, the number of dollars that would be required, at the time the expense is incurred, to acquire the resources consumed. On the balance sheet, the amounts that would have to be paid to replace the assets or satisfy the liabilities as of the balance sheet date.

16. A measure of the changing purchasing power of a dollar spent for a very broad range of items; for example, the Consumer Price Index for All Urban Consumers.

17. Adjustments to previously made assumptions about the future such as salvage values and the length of useful lives of buildings and equipment.

18. A gain or loss that is abnormal and unrelated or only incidentally related to the ordinary activities and environment of the business.

19. A general decrease in the prices paid for goods and services.

20. Money or claims to receive a fixed amount of money; the number of dollars to be received does not change regardless of changes in the purchasing power of the dollar.

21. Operations of a company involving a particular line of business or class of customer, providing the assets, activities, and financial results of the operations can be distinguished from other parts of the business.

22. An indicator of the changing purchasing power of a dollar spent for items in a specific category, including a much narrower range of goods and services than does a general price index.

23. Conventional financial statements that disclose revenues, expenses, assets, liabilities, and owners' equity in terms of the historical monetary units exchanged at the time the transactions occurred.

Part II

Complete the following by filling in the blanks.

1. Changes in accounting estimates _____ (are, are not) prior period adjustments.

2. The results of discontinued operations are separated from the results of other activities on the income statement in order to _____

   _____

   _____ .

3. The cumulative effect on prior years' incomes of a change in accounting principle is reported on the _____ (income statement, statement of retained earnings).

4. Gains or losses from exchange or translation of foreign currencies _____

   _____ (are, are not) considered extraordinary gains or losses.

72

5. If a simple average of the unit prices of several items is calculated for each of two years, a comparison of the averages will indicate the impact of the price changes on most purchasers of those items only if _____ _____ .

6. In the case of an asset about to be sold, the recoverable amount is its _____ _____ .

7. Historical cost/constant dollar accounting is sometimes criticized as being an inadequate response to the problem of changing prices because it does not present _____ _____ in financial statements.

8. The two primary alternatives to conventional accounting that make comprehensive adjustments for the effects of price changes are _____ _____
and _____ .

9. _____ represent money or claims to receive a fixed amount of money with the number of dollars to be received not changing regardless of changes in the purchasing power of the dollar.

10. The requirements for large companies disclosing the effects of changing prices _____ _____ (include, do not include) disclosure of the current cost of inventory at the end of the year.

11. If the general price index was 115 in 198A and was 138 in 198E, it would be appropriate to say that the _____ _____ had fallen by _____% from 198A to 198E.

12. The basic reason why conventional financial statements fail to adequately account for inflation is _____ _____ _____ _____ _____ .

13. _____ is the method of accounting that makes adjustments for specific price changes in nonmonetary assets and liabilities.

14. A _____ measures the relative costs of purchasing a given market basket of items in each of several years or time periods.

15. For accounting purposes, the most important use of a price index is to _____ _____ _____ .

Part III

A product that originally cost $20,000 was later sold for $30,000. At the time of sale, the cost to replace the product was $25,500. Also, the general price index rose from 92 at the time of purchase to 115 at the time of sale. Determine the gross profit from sales assuming (1) historical cost/nominal dollar financial statements; (2) historical cost/constant dollar accounting; and (3) current cost accounting.

	Historical Cost/ Nominal Dollar Statements	Historical Cost/ Constant Dollar Accounting	Current Cost Accounting
Sales			
Cost of sales:			
Gross profit			

Part IV

A company's Cash account showed the following activity and balances during the year:

Balance, January 1	$ 52,000
Receipts from sales	475,000
Payments of expenses	(400,000)
Payment of dividend, December 28	(50,000)
Balance, December 31	$ 77,000

Cash receipts from sales and disbursements for expenses occurred uniformly throughout the year. The general price index during the year was:

January	120
Average during the year	125
December	138

74

Calculate the purchasing power gain or loss from holding cash during the year.

	Historical Cost/ Nominal Dollar Amounts	Restatement Factor from Price Index	Restated to December 31	Gain or Loss
Balance, January 1	$ 52,000			
Receipts from sales	475,000			
Payments of expenses	(400,000)			
Payment of dividend	(50,000)			
Ending balance, adjusted	_____			
Ending balance, actual	$ 77,000			
Purchasing power gain (loss)				

Part I

Part II

1. are not

2. allow statement readers to better evaluate and judge the continuing operations of the business

3. income statement

4. are not

5. those purchasers typically buy an equal number of units of each item

6. net realizable value

7. current values

8. historical cost/constant dollar accounting, current cost accounting

9. Monetary assets

10. include

11. purchasing power of the dollar, 20

12. that transactions are recorded in terms of the historical number of dollars paid, and these amounts are not adjusted even though subsequent changes in prices may dramatically change the value of the items purchased

13. Current cost accounting

14. price-level index

15. restate dollar amounts of cost which were paid in some earlier year into the current price level

Part III

	Historical Cost/ Nominal Dollar Statements	Historical Cost/ Constant Dollar Accounting	Current Cost Accounting
Sales	$30,000	$30,000	$30,000
Cost of sales:	20,000		
$20,000 × (115/92)		25,000	
....			$25,500
Gross profit	$10,000	$ 5,000	$ 4,500

Part IV

	Historical Cost/ Nominal Dollar Amounts	Restatement Factor from Price Index	Restated to December 31	Gain or Loss
Balance, January 1	$ 52,000	138/120	$ 59,800	
Receipts from sales	475,000	138/125	524,400	
Payments of expenses	(400,000)	138/125	(441,600)	
Payment of dividend	(50,000)	138/138	(50,000)	
Ending balance, adjusted			$ 92,600	
Ending balance, actual	$ 77,000		(77,000)	
Purchasing power gain (loss)				$15,600

20

Analyzing Financial Statements

Your objectives in studying this chapter should include learning how to:

List the three broad objectives of financial reporting by business enterprises.

Describe comparative financial statements, how they are prepared, and the limitations associated with interpreting them.

Prepare common-size comparative statements and interpret them.

Explain the importance of working capital in the analysis of financial statements, and list the typical ratios used to analyze working capital.

Calculate the common ratios used in analyzing the balance sheet and income statement, and state what each ratio is intended to measure.

State the limitations associated with using financial statement ratios and the sources from which standards for comparison may be obtained.

Calculate earnings per share for companies with simple capital structures. Explain the difference between primary and fully diluted earnings per share.

Define or explain the words and phrases listed in the chapter Glossary.

Topical Outline

I. Objectives of financial reporting

    A. Financial reporting should provide information:

        1. That is useful to present and potential investors and creditors and other users in making rational investment, credit and similar decisions.

        2. To help present and potential investors and creditors and other users in assessing the amounts, timing, and uncertainty of prospective cash flows.

        3. About the economic resources of an enterprise, the claims to those resources, and the effects of transactions, events, and circumstances that change its resources and claims to those resources.

    B. Conceptual framework—the statement of the objectives of financial reporting is part of the FASB conceptual framework project.

II. Comparative statements

    A. Statements with data for two or more successive accounting periods placed in columns side by side in order to better illustrate changes in the data.

    B. Trend percentages emphasize changes that have occurred from period to period and are useful in comparing data covering a number of years.

    C. Common-size comparative statements—statements in which each amount is expressed as a percentage of a base amount.

III. Analysis of working capital—the amount of working capital is not a measure of a company's ability to meet current debts or take advantage of discounts; the relation of current assets to current liabilities is such a measure.

    A. Current ratio—current assets divided by current liabilities.

    B. Acid-test ratio—quick assets (cash, temporary investments, accounts receivable, and notes receivable) divided by current liabilities.

    C. Accounts receivable turnover—net sales or credit sales divided by average accounts receivable.

    D. Days' sales uncollected—an indication of the speed with which a company collects its accounts; calculated by dividing accounts receivable by net credit sales and then multiplying by 365 days.

    E. Merchandise turnover—the number of times a company's average inventory is sold during an accounting period; calculated by dividing cost of goods sold by average merchandise inventory.

IV. Standards of comparison used by financial analysts

    A. Standards acquired from the analyst's own experience.

    B. Information from other competitive companies in the same industry.

    C. Published data such as that put out by Dun & Bradstreet.

    D. Information published by local and national trade associations.

    E. Rule-of-thumb standards.

V. Other balance sheet and income statement relationships

    A. Capital contributions of creditors and owners—shows the percentage of total liabilities and owners' equity supplied by creditors and owners.

    B. Pledged plant assets to secured liabilities—measures the protection provided the secured creditors by the pledged assets.

    C. Times fixed interest charges earned—measures the security of the return to bondholders or mortgage holders; calculated by dividing income before fixed interest charges and income taxes by fixed interest charges.

D. Rate of return on total assets employed—measures management's performance; calculated as income before interest and income taxes divided by average total assets employed.

E. Rate of return on common stockholders' equity—calculated as net income (minus preferred dividend requirements, if any) divided by average common stockholders' equity.

VI. Earnings per share—one of the most commonly reported figures in the financial press.

A. For companies with simple capital structures, it is calculated as net income (minus preferred dividend requirements, if the company has nonconvertible preferred shares outstanding) divided by the weighted-average number of common shares outstanding.

B. For companies with complex capital structures, two types of earnings per share calculations are often required:

1. Primary earnings per share
2. Fully diluted earnings per share

C. Generally accepted accounting principles require that earnings per share data be shown on the face of published income statements for:

1. Income from continuing operations.
2. Gains or losses from discontinued operations.
3. Extraordinary items.
4. Cumulative effect of changes in accounting principles.
5. Net income.

D. Price-Earnings Ratio

1. Commonly used in comparing investment opportunities.
2. Calculated by dividing market price per share by earnings per share.

Part I

Many of the important ideas and concepts discussed in Chapter 20 are reflected in the following list of key terms. Test your understanding of these terms by matching the appropriate definitions with the terms. Record the number identifying the most appropriate definition in the blank space next to each term.

_____ Accounts receivable turnover

_____ Acid-test ratio

_____ Antidilutive securities

_____ Common-size comparative statements

_____ Common stock equivalent

_____ Comparative statement

_____ Complex capital structure

_____ Current ratio

_____ Dilutive securities

_____ Earnings per share

_____ Financial reporting

_____ Fully diluted earnings per share

_____ General purpose financial statements

_____ Merchandise turnover

_____ Price-earnings ratio

_____ Primary earnings per share

_____ Quick ratio

_____ Rate of return on common stockholders' equity

_____ Rate of return on total assets employed

_____ Simple capital structure

_____ Times fixed interest charges earned

1. A capital structure that includes securities which are convertible into common stock.

2. Convertible securities that would reduce earnings per share if they had been converted at the beginning of the period.

3. The amount of net income (or components of income) that accrues to common shares divided by the weighted-average number of common shares outstanding.

4. The relation of a company's current assets to its current liabilities, that is, current assets divided by current liabilities.

5. The process of preparing and issuing financial information about a company.

6. A convertible security the eventual conversion of which appears, at the time of issuance, to be very probable.

7. A financial statement with data for two or more successive accounting periods placed in columns side by side in order to better illustrate changes in the data.

8. Earnings per share statistics that are calculated as if all dilutive securities had already been converted.

9. A synonym for acid-test ratio.

10. Comparative financial statements in which each amount is expressed as a percentage of a base amount. In the balance sheet, total assets is usually selected as the base amount and is expressed as 100%. In the income statement, net sales is usually selected as the base amount.

11. An indication of how long it takes a company to collect its accounts, calculated by dividing net sales or credit sales by the average accounts receivable balance.

12. Earnings per share statistics that are calculated as if dilutive, common stock equivalents had already been converted at the beginning of the period.

13. Financial statements (usually including the income statement, balance sheet, statement of retained earnings, and statement of changes in financial position) published by a company for use by persons who do not have the ability to obtain specialized financial reports designed to meet their interests.

14. Market price per share of common stock divided by earnings per share.

15. Net income after taxes and dividends on preferred stock divided by average common stockholders' equity.

16. An indicator of a company's ability to satisfy fixed interest charges, calculated as net income before fixed interest charges and income taxes divided by fixed interest charges.

17. The number of times a company's average inventory is sold during an accounting period, calculated by dividing cost of goods sold by the average merchandise inventory balance.

18. A capital structure that includes only common stock and perhaps nonconvertible preferred stock.

19. The relation of quick assets, such as cash, temporary investments, accounts receivable, and notes receivable, to current liabilities, calculated as quick assets divided by current liabilities.

20. Convertible securities that would increase earnings per share if they had been converted at the beginning of the period.

21. Income before interest and income taxes, expressed as a percentage of the average amount of total assets employed during the period.

Part II

Bartlett Company had 20,000 shares of common stock outstanding at the beginning of 198A. On April 1, the company sold 20,000 additional shares of its common stock, and on November 1 the company declared a 2 for 1 stock split. Calculate the weighted-average number of common shares outstanding during the year.

Part III

The sales, cost of goods sold, and gross profits from sales of the Laker Company for a five-year period are shown below:

	198A	198B	198C	198D	198E
Sales	$350,000	$385,000	$413,000	$455,000	$497,000
Cost of goods sold	250,000	280,000	305,000	345,000	375,000
Gross profit	$100,000	$105,000	$108,000	$110,000	$122,000

Laker Company's sales are expressed in trend percentages below. Express its cost of goods sold and gross profit in trend percentages in the spaces provided.

	198A	198B	198C	198D	198E
Sales	100	110	118	130	142
Cost of goods sold					
Gross profit					

Comment on the situation shown by the data:

_____

_____

_____

_____

_____

Part IV

Complete the following by filling in the blanks.

1. When calculating accounts receivable turnover, the sales number that should be used is _____ (cash, credit, total) sales.

2. The acid-test ratio is calculated by dividing _____
   by _____ . This ratio is a check
   on _____ .

3. Merchandise turnover is calculated by dividing _____
   _____ by _____ .
   It is an indication of _____
   _____ .

4. A slower turnover of merchandise inventory _____ (will, will not) tend to increase working capital requirements.

5. The current ratio is calculated by dividing _____
   _____ by _____ . It is
   an indication of _____ with which a company
   can meet its current obligations.

6. When the conversion of a security (such as preferred stock into common stock) reduces earnings per share, the security is said to be _____ ;
   those that increase earnings per share are _____ .

7. The rate of return on total assets employed is calculated by dividing _____
   _____ plus _____ by
   _____ amount of assets employed during the year.

8. Times fixed interest charges earned is calculated by dividing income before deducting
   _____ and _____
   _____ by the amount of the _____
   _____ .

9. Days' sales uncollected are calculated by dividing _____
   _____ by _____
   and multiplying the resulting quotient by _____
   _____ . Days' sales uncollected are an indication of _____
   _____
   _____ .

10. The price-earnings ratio for a company's common stock is calculated by dividing the
    _____ per share of the common stock by
    _____ per share of common stock.

11. The rate of return on common stockholders' equity is calculated by dividing _____ _____ by _____ _____ stockholders' equity.

12. For companies with simple capital structures, earnings per share is calculated by dividing _____ by _____ _____ .

13. Compared to companies with an average growth rate, companies in a growth industry would be expected to have a _____ (higher, lower) price-earnings ratio.

Part V

1. Following are the condensed income statements of two companies of unequal size.

   Examine the statement amounts and write in this space (_____) the name of the company that operated more efficiently. If you cannot tell from examining the statement amounts, write "cannot tell" in the blank.

COMPANIES A AND Z
Income Statements for Year Ended December 31, 19—

	Company A	Company Z
Sales	$325,000	$265,000
Cost of goods sold	204,750	164,300
Gross profit on sales	$120,250	$100,700
Selling expenses	$ 61,750	$ 49,025
Administrative expenses	42,250	34,450
Total operating expenses	$104,000	$ 83,475
Net income	$ 16,250	$ 17,225

2. Common-size percentages are often used in comparing the statements of companies of unequal size. Below are the condensed income statements of Companies A and Z with the income statement amounts of Company A already expressed in common-size percentages. Express the income statement amounts of Company Z in common-size percentages in the spaces provided.

COMPANIES A AND Z
Income Statements for Year Ended December 31, 19—

	Dollar Amounts		Common-Size Percentages	
	Company A	Company Z	Company A	Company Z
Sales	$325,000	$265,000	100.0%	%
Cost of goods sold	204,750	164,300	63.0	
Gross profit on sales	$120,250	$100,700	37.0	
Selling expenses	$ 61,750	$ 49,025	19.0	
Administrative expenses	42,250	34,450	13.0	
Total operating expenses	$104,000	$ 83,475	32.0	
Net income	$ 16,250	$ 17,225	5.0	

3. After expressing the Company Z income statement amounts in common-size percentages, examine the common-size percentages of the two companies and write in this space (_____) the name of the company that operated more efficiently.

Part I

Part II

Time period	Shares outstanding adjusted for stock split		Portion of year		
January - March	20,000 × 2	×	3/12	=	10,000
April - December	(20,000 + 20,000) × 2	×	9/12	=	60,000
Weighted-average common shares outstanding			....		70,000

Part III

	198A	198B	198C	198D	198E
Sales	100	110	118	130	142
Cost of goods sold	100	112	122	138	150
Gross profit	100	105	108	110	122

Laker Company's sales increased each year throughout the five-year period, but its cost of goods sold increased more rapidly. This slowed the rate of increase in its gross profit.

Part IV

1. credit
2. quick assets, current liabilities, the ability to pay debts that mature in the very near future
3. cost of goods sold, average inventory, merchandising efficiency
4. will
5. current assets, current liabilities, the ease
6. dilutive; antidilutive

7. income, interest expense, the average

8. income taxes, fixed interest charges, fixed interest charges

9. accounts receivable, charge sales, the number of days in a year, collection efficiency (the speed with which a company collects its accounts)

10. market price, earnings

11. net income less any preferred dividends, average common

12. net income minus preferred dividends, if any; the weighted-average number of common shares outstanding

13. higher

Part V

1 The average person cannot tell from an examination of the figures which company operated more efficiently.

2.

COMPANIES A AND Z
Income Statements for Year Ended December 31, 19—

	Dollar Amounts		Common-Size Percentages	
	Company A	Company Z	Company A	Company Z
Sales	$325,000	$265,000	100.0	100.0
Cost of goods sold	204,750	164,300	63.0	62.0
Gross profit on sales	$120,250	$100,700	37.0	38.0
Selling expenses	$ 61,750	$ 49,025	19.0	18.5
Administrative expenses	42,250	34,450	13.0	13.0
Total operating expenses	$104,000	$ 83,475	32.0	31.5
Net income	$ 16,250	$ 17,225	5.0	6.5

3. Company Z

21

Accounting for Manufacturing Companies

Your objectives in studying this chapter should include learning how to:

Describe the basic differences in the financial statements of manufacturing companies and merchandising companies.

Describe the procedures inherent in a general accounting system for a manufacturing company.

List the different accounts which appear on a manufacturing company's books and state what the accounts represent.

Explain the purpose of a manufacturing statement, how one is composed, and how the statement is integrated with the primary financial statements.

Prepare financial statements for a manufacturing company from a work sheet.

Prepare the adjusting and closing entries for a manufacturing company.

Explain the procedures for assigning costs to the different manufacturing inventories.

Define or explain the words and phrases listed in the chapter Glossary.

Topical Outline

I. Manufacturing accounting systems

   A. Compared with merchandising accounting systems

      1. Both depend upon the sale of one or more commodities or products for revenue.

      2. A merchandising company buys the goods it sells in the same condition in which they are sold and records the cost in the Purchases account.

      3. A manufacturing company buys raw materials which it manufactures into the finished products it sells. Then, it combines the balances of a number of material, labor, and overhead accounts to determine the cost of the goods it has manufactured for sale.

   B. Compared with a cost accounting system

      1. A general accounting system:

         a. Uses periodic physical inventories.

         b. Focuses on the determination of total cost of all goods manufactured each period.

      2. A cost accounting system:

         a. Uses perpetual inventories.

         b. Focuses on the determination of the unit cost of manufacturing a product or performing a service.

II. Manufacturing costs and accounts

   A. Elements of manufacturing costs

      1. Direct materials

         a. Direct materials—the commodities that enter into and become part of a finished product; easily traced to units of product or batches of production.

         b. Indirect materials—commodities that generally do not enter into or become a part of the finished product; materials used in the manufacturing process which are not easily traced to specific units or batches of production, and accounted for as factory overhead.

         c. Raw materials—commodities usually intended for use in the production process as direct materials. Commodities purchased for use as indirect materials are debited to a Factory Supplies account.

      2. Direct labor

         a. Direct labor—the labor of those who work specifically on the materials being converted into finished products.

         b. Indirect labor—labor used in the manufacturing process but not applied specifically to the finished product.

      3. Factory overhead—all manufacturing costs other than direct materials and direct labor costs.

   B. Product costs and period costs

      1. Product costs—costs that are assigned to units of product and include all manufacturing costs (direct materials, direct labor, and factory overhead).

      2. Period costs—costs that are assigned to expense accounts and include all selling and administrative expenses not part of the manufacturing operation.

C. Accounts unique to a manufacturing company

    1. Raw Material Purchases—debited for the cost of all raw materials.
    2. Raw Materials Inventory—debited (through a closing entry) for the cost of raw materials on hand at the end of each accounting period.
    3. Goods in Process Inventory—debited (through a closing entry) for the cost of partially finished products at the end of the accounting period.
    4. Finished Goods Inventory—equivalent to the Merchandise Inventory account of a merchandising company; debited (through a closing entry) for the cost of the amount of finished goods on hand at the end of the accounting period.

III. Income statement of a manufacturing company—similar to that of a merchandising concern except:

A. In the cost of goods sold section "Cost of goods manufactured" replaces the "Purchases" element.
B. Finished goods inventories take the place of merchandise inventories.

IV. Manufacturing statement

A. Contains a calculation of the cost of goods manufactured and has four sections:

    1. Cost of direct materials used.
    2. Cost of direct labor used.
    3. Factory overhead costs incurred.
    4. Allocation of total costs incurred between the change in goods in process inventory and the cost of goods manufactured.

B. Cost of goods manufactured is added (on the income statement) to the beginning-of-period finished goods inventory to determine goods available for sale.

V. Work sheet for a manufacturing company

A. Two additional columns are provided for the Manufacturing Statement.
B. Adjustments are the same as for a merchandising company.
C. The trial balance and adjustments amounts are sorted to the appropriate Manufacturing Statement, Income Statement, and Balance Sheet columns.
D. End-of-period raw materials, goods in process, and finished goods inventories are inserted in the appropriate columns.

VI. Closing entries

A. All accounts containing manufacturing costs are closed to Manufacturing Summary.
B. Manufacturing Summary is closed to Income Summary, along with other expenses.

VII. Inventory valuation—manufacturing company

A. Raw materials inventories valuation presents no problem; items are in same form purchased.
B. Values of goods in process and finished goods inventories must be estimated by adding together estimates of direct materials, direct labor, and factory overhead costs applicable to each item.

Part I

Many of the important ideas and concepts discussed in Chapter 21 are reflected in the following list of key terms. Test your understanding of these terms by matching the appropriate definitions with the terms. Record the number identifying the most appropriate definition in the blank space next to each term.

_____ Cost accounting system   _____ Indirect materials

_____ Direct labor   _____ Manufacturing overhead

_____ Direct materials   _____ Manufacturing statement

_____ Factory burden   _____ Period costs

_____ Factory overhead   _____ Product costs

_____ Finished goods   _____ Raw materials

_____ General accounting system for manufacturers   _____ Schedule of the cost of goods manufactured

_____ Goods in process   _____ Work in process

_____ Indirect labor

1. Costs that are assigned to units of product and reported in the balance sheet as inventories and in the income statement as cost of goods sold; included are all manufacturing costs.

2. Manufactured products that have been completed and are ready for sale; the equivalent of a store's merchandise.

3. Commodities, such as oil for machinery, that are used in production but that are not easily traced to specific units or batches of production; accounted for as factory overhead.

4. An accounting system that uses perpetual inventories in accounting for manufacturing operations and is designed to assist management's efforts to control costs.

5. A synonym for manufacturing statement.

6. Products in the process of being manufactured that have received a portion or all of their materials and have had some labor and overhead applied but that are not completed.

7. A synonym for goods in process.

8. Commodities that enter into and become a part of a finished product; therefore, commodities the cost of which is easily traced to units of product or batches of production.

9. A schedule showing the costs incurred to manufacture a product or products during a period.

10. Commodities that are purchased for use in the manufacturing process, normally as direct materials. Occasionally used as indirect materials.

11. An accounting system that uses periodic inventories to determine the total cost of all goods manufactured during each accounting period.

12. A synonym for factory overhead. Also called factory burden.

13. The labor of those people who work specifically on the conversion of direct materials into finished products; in other words, labor that can be easily associated with and charged to units or batches of production.

14. Costs that are not incurred as part of manufacturing operations and that are charged to expense in the periods they are incurred.

95

15. The labor of superintendents, foremen, millwrights, engineers, janitors, and others that contribute to production but do not work specifically on the manufactured products; therefore, labor that cannot be easily associated with specific units of product.

16. All manufacturing costs other than for direct materials and direct labor.

17. A synonym for factory overhead or manufacturing overhead.

Part II

The unfinished work sheet of Karmen Corporation appears on page 97. You should assume that no adjustments are needed.

The company's year-end inventories for the year of the work sheet are: raw materials, $28,500; goods in process, $20,700; and finished goods, $25,500.

1. Since there are no adjustments, sort the trial balance amounts to the proper Manufacturing Statement, Income Statement, and Balance Sheet columns, and complete the work sheet.
2. After finishing the work sheet, use its information to complete the following Manufacturing Statement and the Income Statement at the top of page 98.

KARMEN CORPORATION

Manufacturing Statement

For the Year Ended December 31, 19—

Direct materials:						
Raw materials inventory, January 1, 19—						
Raw material purchases						
Raw materials available for use						
Raw materials inventory, December 31, 19—						
Direct materials used						
Direct labor						
Factory overhead costs:						
Indirect labor						
Machinery repairs						
Factory supplies used						
Small tools written off						
Depreciation of machinery						
Total factory overhead costs						
Total manufacturing costs						
Add: Goods in process inventory, January 1, 19—						
Total goods in process during the year						
Deduct: Goods in process inventory,						
December 31, 19—						
Cost of goods manufactured						

KARMEN CORPORATION
Work Sheet for Year Ended December 31, 19—

ACCOUNT TITLES	TRIAL BALANCE DR.	TRIAL BALANCE CR.	ADJUSTMENTS DR.	ADJUSTMENTS CR.	MFG. STATEMENT DR.	MFG. STATEMENT CR.	INCOME STATEMENT DR.	INCOME STATEMENT CR.	BALANCE SHEET DR.	BALANCE SHEET CR.
Cash	23,100 00									
Raw materials inventory	22,200 00									
Goods in process inventory	18,600 00									
Finished goods inventory	25,800 00									
Factory supplies	600 00									
Prepaid factory insurance	900 00									
Small tools	2,400 00									
Machinery	143,100 00									
Accumulated depreciation, machinery		20,700 00								
Accounts payable		7,800 00								
Common stock, $10 par value		150,000 00								
Retained earnings		20,100 00								
Sales		289,200 00								
Raw material purchases	96,000 00									
Direct labor	55,800 00									
Indirect labor	24,900 00									
Machinery repairs	1,800 00									
Selling expenses	36,900 00									
Administrative expenses	25,200 00									
Factory supplies used	3,300 00									
Small tools written off	600 00									
Depreciation of machinery	6,600 00									
	487,800 00	487,800 00								
Cost of goods manufactured to Income Statement columns										
Net income										

KARMEN CORPORATION

Income Statement

For the Year Ended December 31, 19—

Revenue:							
Sales							
Cost of goods sold:							
Finished goods inventory, January 1, 19—							
Cost of goods manufactured							
Goods available for sale							
Finished goods inventory, December 31, 19—							
Cost of goods sold							
Gross profit from sales							
Operating expenses:							
Selling expenses							
Administrative expenses							
Total operating expenses							
Net income							
Net income per common share							

3. After completing the manufacturing and income statements, prepare adjusting entries for inventories and entries to close the company's manufacturing statement and income statement accounts.

DATE	ACCOUNT TITLES AND EXPLANATION	P.R.	DEBIT	CREDIT

DATE	ACCOUNT TITLES AND EXPLANATION	P.R.	DEBIT	CREDIT

Part III

Karmen Corporation of Part II manufactures a single product. On the Study Guide date it had 1,700 units of the product in its finished goods inventory, which is valued at $15.00 per unit or a total of $25,500. (See Part II on page 96.) In arriving at the $15.00 per unit value, the company examined the units and estimated that each unit contained $7 of direct material and that $5.00 of direct labor had been applied. The company then examined the relation between its total direct labor costs and its total overhead costs for the year (look at the manufacturing statement on page 96), and found that it had incurred $55,800 of direct labor cost and $37,200 of overhead costs or

that its overhead costs were _____ % of its direct labor costs. It then multiplied

$4.50 (the direct labor cost per unit) by _____ % to arrive at an estimated $3.00 per unit overhead cost. After this it added the $7 of estimated direct material cost plus the $5.00 of estimated direct labor cost plus the $3.00 of estimated overhead cost to get the

$ _____ estimated cost per unit for its 1,500 units of finished goods.

Part I

Part II

KARMEN CORPORATION

Manufacturing Statement

For Year Ended December 31, 19—

Direct materials:		
Raw materials inventory, January 1, 19—	$ 22,200	
Raw material purchases	96,000	
Raw materials available for use	$118,200	
Raw materials inventory, December 31, 19—	28,500	
Direct materials used		$ 89,700
Direct labor		55,800
Factory overhead costs:		
Indirect labor	$ 24,900	
Machinery repairs	1,800	
Factory supplies used	3,300	
Small tools written off	600	
Depreciation of machinery	6,600	
Total factory overhead costs		37,200
Total manufacturing costs		$182,700
Add goods in process inventory, January 1, 19—		18,600
Total goods in process during the year		$201,300
Deduct goods in process inventory, December 31, 19—		20,700
Cost of goods manufactured		$180,600

Work Sheet for Year Ended December 31, 19—

ACCOUNT TITLES	TRIAL BALANCE DR.	TRIAL BALANCE CR.	ADJUSTMENTS DR.	ADJUSTMENTS CR.	MFG. STATEMENT DR.	MFG. STATEMENT CR.	INCOME STATEMENT DR.	INCOME STATEMENT CR.	BALANCE SHEET DR.	BALANCE SHEET CR.
Cash	23,100 00								23,100 00	
Raw materials inventory	22,200 00					28,500 00			28,500 00	
Goods in process inventory	18,600 00					20,700 00			20,700 00	
Finished goods inventory	25,800 00						25,800 00	25,500 00	25,500 00	
Factory supplies	600 00								600 00	
Prepaid factory insurance	900 00								900 00	
Small tools	2,400 00								2,400 00	
Machinery	143,100 00								143,100 00	
Accumulated depreciation, machinery		20,700 00								20,700 00
Accounts payable		7,800 00								7,800 00
Common stock, $10 par value		150,000 00								150,000 00
Retained earnings		20,100 00								20,100 00
Sales		289,200 00						289,200 00		
Raw material purchases	96,000 00				96,000 00					
Direct labor	55,800 00				55,800 00					
Indirect labor	24,900 00				24,900 00					
Machinery repairs	1,800 00				1,800 00					
Selling expenses	36,900 00						36,900 00			
Administrative expenses	25,200 00						25,200 00			
Factory supplies used	3,300 00				3,300 00					
Small tools written off	600 00				600 00					
Depreciation of machinery	6,600 00				6,600 00					
	487,800 00	487,800 00			229,800 00	49,200 00				
Cost of goods manufactured to Income Statement columns						180,600 00	180,600 00			
					229,800 00	229,800 00	268,500 00	314,700 00	244,800 00	198,600 00
Net income							46,200 00			46,200 00
							314,700 00	314,700 00	244,800 00	244,800 00

KARMEN CORPORATION
Income Statement
For Year Ended December 31, 19—

Revenue:		
Sales		$289,200
Cost of goods sold:		
Finished goods inventory, January 1, 19—	$ 25,800	
Cost of goods manufactured (see Manufacturing Statement)	180,600	
Goods available for sale	$206,400	
Finished goods inventory, December 31, 19—	25,500	
Cost of goods sold		180,900
Gross profit from sales		$108,300
Operating expenses:		
Selling expenses	$ 36,900	
Administrative expenses	25,200	
Total operating expenses		62,100
Net income		$ 46,200
Net income per common share		$3.08

Closing entries:

Dec. 31	Manufacturing Summary		229,800.00	
		Raw Materials Inventory		22,200.00
		Goods in Process Inventory		18,600.00
		Raw Material Purchases		96,000.00
		Direct Labor		55,800.00
		Indirect Labor		24,900.00
		Machinery Repairs		1,800.00
		Factory Supplies Used		3,300.00
		Small Tools Written Off		600.00
		Depreciation of Machinery		6,600.00
31	Raw Materials Inventory		28,500.00	
	Goods in Process Inventory		20,700.00	
		Manufacturing Summary		49,200.00
31	Income Summary		268,500.00	
		Finished Goods Inventory		25,800.00
		Selling Expenses		36,900.00
		Administrative Expenses		25,200.00
		Manufacturing Summary		180,600.00
31	Finished Goods Inventory		25,500.00	
	Sales		289,200.00	
		Income Summary		314,700.00
31	Income Summary		46,200.00	
		Retained Earnings		46,200.00

Part III

66–2/3, 66–2/3, $15.00

22

Cost Accounting,
Job Order,
and Process

Your objectives in studying this chapter should include learning how to:

State the conditions under which job order cost accounting should be used and those under which process cost accounting should be used.

Describe how costs for individual jobs are accumulated on job cost sheets and how control accounts are charged with the total costs of all jobs.

Allocate overhead to jobs and distribute any over- or underapplied overhead.

Describe how costs are accumulated by departments under process costing.

Explain what an equivalent finished unit is and how equivalent finished units are used in calculating unit costs.

Prepare a process cost summary.

Define or explain the words and phrases listed in the chapter Glossary.

Topical Outline

I. Job order cost accounting

   A. Accumulating costs by job

      1. Costs are accumulated in terms of a job or a job lot (a special order for a customer or a quantity of identical items).

      2. A job cost sheet is maintained for each job. The job cost sheets for the jobs in process make up a subsidiary ledger called the Job Cost Ledger.

      3. The Job Cost Ledger is controlled by the Goods in Process account in the General Ledger.

   B. Accounting for materials

      1. Raw materials are requested for use on specific jobs by submitting a materials requisition to the materials storeroom keeper.

      2. The cost of raw materials listed on each materials requisition is recorded (in the Direct Materials column) on the appropriate job cost sheet.

      3. Raw materials used for overhead tasks are charged to accounts listed in the Factory Overhead Ledger.

   C. Accounting for labor

      1. Labor time tickets are used to record the labor charged to specific jobs and to overhead.

      2. The Factory Payroll account balance is transferred partially to Goods in Process (for direct labor) and partially to Factory Overhead (for indirect labor).

   D. Accounting for overhead

      1. A predetermined overhead application rate is calculated as next year's estimated overhead costs divided by next year's estimated direct labor costs.

      2. Overhead is charged to specific jobs on the basis of the direct labor applied to each job.

      3. At year-end, underapplied or overapplied overhead is allocated to goods in process, finished goods, and cost of goods sold.

II. Process cost accounting

   A. Accumulating costs by department

      1. Direct materials, direct labor, and factory overhead costs are charged to specific production departments in which units of product are processed.

      2. A separate goods in process account is used for the costs of each department.

      3. Departmental production is measured in terms of equivalent finished units.

   B. Calculating unit costs

      1. Direct materials costs incurred by a department are allocated equally to the equivalent finished units for direct materials.

      2. Direct labor costs and usually factory overhead are allocated equally to equivalent finished units for direct labor.

   C. The process cost summary is a departmental report that summarizes:

      1. The costs charged to the department.

      2. The equivalent unit processing costs of the department.

      3. The assignment of costs to the work of the department.

Part I

Many of the important ideas and concepts discussed in Chapter 22 are reflected in the following list of key terms. Test your understanding of these terms by matching the appropriate definitions with the terms. Record the number identifying the most appropriate definition in the blank space next to each term.

_____ Cost accounting system

_____ Equivalent finished units

_____ Job

_____ Job Cost Ledger

_____ Job cost sheet

_____ Job lot

_____ Job order cost system

_____ Labor time ticket

_____ Materials consumption report

_____ Materials requisition

_____ Overapplied overhead

_____ Predetermined overhead application rate

_____ Process cost system

_____ Underapplied overhead

1. A system of accounting for manufacturing costs in which costs are assembled in terms of processes or steps in manufacturing a product.

2. A subsidiary ledger to the Goods in Process account in which are kept the job cost sheets of unfinished jobs.

3. A record of how an employee's time at work was used; the record serves as the basis for charging jobs and overhead accounts for the employee's wages.

4. An accounting system based on perpetual inventory records that is designed to emphasize the determination of unit costs and the control of costs.

5. The amount by which actual overhead incurred exceeds the overhead applied to production, based on a predetermined application rate and evidenced by a debit balance in the Factory Overhead account at the end of the period.

6. A document, given to the materials storeroom keeper in exchange for raw materials, that has the purpose of enhancing control over materials and providing a means of charging the cost of raw materials to jobs, or processing departments, or factory overhead; the document identifies the materials needed for a specific job, processing department, or purpose and the account to which the materials cost should be charged.

7. A special production order of a unique product, often manufactured especially for and to the specifications of a customer.

8. A rate that is used to charge overhead cost to production; calculated by relating estimated overhead cost for a period to another variable such as estimated direct labor cost.

9. A measure of production with respect to direct materials or direct labor (and overhead), expressed as the number of units that could have been manufactured from start to finish during a period given the amount of direct materials or direct labor (and overhead) used during the period.

10. The amount by which overhead applied on the basis of a predetermined overhead application rate exceeds overhead actually incurred.

11. A record of the costs incurred on a single job.

12. A system of accounting for manufacturing costs in which costs are assembled in terms of jobs or job lots.

13. A document, kept by the materials storeroom keeper as a substitute for materials requisitions, the purpose of which is to show the raw materials issued to each department during a cost period and to provide the information necessary to prepare journal entries charging materials costs to the appropriate accounts.

14. A job that consists of a quantity of identical items.

Part II

Complete the following by filling in the blanks.

1. In a process cost system costs are assembled by _____ , with a separate Goods in Process account being used to assemble the costs of each _____ _____ .

2. When overhead is to be applied to jobs on the basis of direct labor cost, a predetermined overhead application rate is established before a cost period begins by estimating the number of dollars of _____ that will be incurred during the period, estimating the number of dollars of _____ _____ that will be incurred during the same period, and then dividing the _____ by the _____ .

3. The heart of a job order cost system is a subsidiary ledger of _____ _____ with a separate cost sheet being used to accumulate the _____ , _____ , and _____ costs of each job.

4. The company of Illustration 22-8 on page 797 of the text is assumed to make a product from metal that is cut to size in a cutting department and assembled in an assembly department; and the company's finished product results from the completion in turn of the cutting and assembly processes.

   Also, in the cost system of the company of Illustration 22-8 _____ are transferred and advanced from the Goods in Process account of one department to the Goods in Process account of the next, just as the product is transferred and advanced in the company's manufacturing procedure. Furthermore, the cost of the finished product in this company is the sum of the costs accumulated in the _____ .

5. Raw materials costs are associated with jobs by means of _____ _____ requisitions, and direct labor costs are associated with jobs by means of _____ time tickets; but to associate overhead costs with jobs it is necessary to assume that the overhead chargeable to a job is related to, for example, the cost of the direct labor used in completing the job, and to use a(n) _____ _____ rate in associating the overhead.

6. If the year-end balance of the Factory Overhead account is a material amount, it is reasonable to dispose of it by _____ among the goods still in process, the finished goods inventory, and cost of goods sold. However, if the amount is immaterial it may be charged to _____ _____ .

110

7. At the end of each day the time tickets of that day are sent to the accounting department where the direct labor time tickets are charged to _____ on the job cost sheets and the indirect labor time tickets are charged to overhead cost accounts in the subsidiary Factory Overhead Ledger.

8. When overhead is applied to jobs on the basis of a predetermined overhead application rate, the number of dollars of overhead applied to jobs during a year will seldom be the same as the number of dollars of overhead actually incurred during the year. Consequently, if more overhead is incurred than is applied to jobs, overhead is said to be _____ _____ (overapplied, underapplied); and if more overhead is applied to jobs than is incurred, overhead is said to be _____ _____ .

9. To gain control over direct materials in a job cost system, all raw materials purchased are placed in a materials _____ where they are kept until needed in production.

10. When a department begins and ends a cost period with partially processed units of product, its production for a cost period must be measured on the basis of _____ _____ .

11. When raw materials are needed on a job, a materials _____ _____ is prepared and signed by a foreman or other responsible person, and is given to the storeroom keeper in exchange for the raw materials.

12. The idea of an equivalent finished unit is based on the assumption that it takes the same amount of direct labor, for example, to one-fourth finish each of _____ _____ units of product as it does to complete one unit.

13. Materials requisitions for such things as machinery lubricants, cleaning materials, and light bulbs are used to charge the costs of these indirect materials to the _____ _____ account.

14. The materials requisitions given to the storeroom keeper in exchange for raw materials to be used on a job are sent to the accounting department where they are used to charge the cost of the raw materials to the job on the job's _____ sheet. The requisitions are also used to make entries in the Raw Materials Ledger to reduce the book record of the amount of _____ on hand, and they are the basis for the entry to charge the Goods in Process account for the cost of all the _____ used on jobs during the cost period.

15. _____ tickets are used to charge jobs and factory overhead accounts with the cost of labor. Throughout each day a new time ticket is prepared each time an employee is changed from one job or overhead task to another. Each time ticket shows the elapsed _____ the employee spent working on the job or task and the cost of his wages for the elapsed _____ .

16. In a job order cost accounting system, a job is a construction project, machine, or other product manufactured especially for and to the _____ _____ of a customer. It may also be a quantity of identical items called a _____ of product.

17. When a predetermined overhead application rate is used in charging overhead to jobs, as soon as the job is completed: (a) The cost of the direct materials used on the job is determined by adding the amounts in the _____ column of the job's cost sheet. (b) Next, the cost of the direct labor applicable to the job is determined by adding the amounts in the _____ column of the cost sheet. (c) Then the overhead applicable to the job is determined by multiplying the job's direct labor cost by the _____ _____ .

Part III

During a cost period a department finished and transferred 63,000 units of product to finished goods, of which 18,000 were in process in the department one-fourth finished when the period began and 45,000 were begun and completed during the period. In addition the department had 13,500 units of product in process, two-thirds processed when the period ended. *Required*: Complete the following calculation of equivalent finished units for this department:

	Units Involved	Fraction Completed during the Period	Equivalent Units Completed
Beginning inventory units			
Units started and finished			
Ending inventory			
Equivalent finished units			

Under the assumption that the foregoing department had $54,000 of direct labor charged to it during the cost period and direct labor is added to the product of the department evenly throughout the process, complete the following calculation of the cost of an equivalent unit of direct labor in this department.

$54,000 / _____ Equivalent Units = $ _____ per Equivalent Unit

After determining the cost of an equivalent unit of direct labor in this department, use this cost in completing the following calculation apportioning the $54,000 of direct labor cost between the department's inventories and its units finished:

Beginning inventory (_____ equivalent units @ $ _____) $ _____

Units started and finished (_____ equivalent units @ $ _____) _____

Ending inventory (_____ equivalent units @ $ _____) _____

Total direct labor charged to the department $54,000

Part I

Part II

1. departments, department
2. direct labor cost, overhead costs, overhead costs, direct labor costs
3. job cost sheets, direct materials, direct labor, factory overhead
4. costs, two departments
5. materials, labor, predetermined overhead application
6. apportioning it, Cost of Goods Sold
7. jobs
8. underapplied, overapplied
9. storeroom
10. equivalent finished units
11. requisition
12. four
13. Factory Overhead
14. cost, raw materials, direct materials
15. Labor time, time, time
16. specifications, job lot
17. (a) Direct Materials, (b) Direct Labor, (c) overhead application rate

Part III

Beginning inventory units	18,000	3/4	13,500
Units started and finished	45,000	all	45,000
Ending inventory	13,500	2/3	9,000
Equivalent finished units			67,500

67,500 Equivalent Units, $0.80 per Equivalent Unit

Beginning inventory (13,500 equivalent units @ $0.80) $10,800
Units started and finished (45,000 equivalent units @ $0.80) 36,000
Ending inventory (9,000 equivalent units @ $0.80) 7,200

23

Accounting for the Segments and Departments of a Business; Responsibility Accounting

Your objectives in studying this chapter should include learning how to:

Describe the segmental information disclosed in the financial reports of large companies having operations in several lines of business.

List the four basic issues faced by accountants in developing segmental information.

State the reasons for departmentalization of businesses.

Describe the types of expenses that should be allocated among departments, the bases for allocating such expenses, and the procedures involved in the allocation process.

Explain the differences between reports designed to measure the profitability of a department and reports that are used to evaluate the performance of a department manager.

Describe the problems associated with allocation of joint costs between departments.

Define or explain the words and phrases listed in the chapter Glossary.

Topical Outline

I. Segmental reporting and departmental accounting—provide information about the parts of a business

   A. Segmental reporting—generally used in reference to published information about the different industries and geographical areas in which a company does business; it is intended primarily for the use of outsiders who are interested in an overall evaluation of the business.

   B. Departmental accounting—relates to information on the subunits of a business prepared for internal managers responsible for planning and controlling the operations of the business.

II. Reporting on broad business segments

   A. Large firms operating in more than one industry must report the following information on each industrial segment:

      1. Revenues.
      2. Operating profits (before interest and taxes).
      3. Identifiable assets.
      4. Capital expenditures.
      5. Depreciation and amortization expense.

   B. Four basic issues faced by companies in developing segmental information:

      1. Identifying significant segments.
      2. Transfer pricing between segments.
      3. Measuring segmental profitability.
      4. Identifying segmental assets.

III. Departmental accounting for internal managers—characterized by two primary goals:

   A. To provide information that management can use in evaluating the profitability or cost effectiveness of each department.

   B. To assign costs and expenses to the particular managers who are responsible for controlling those costs and expenses.

IV. Departmentalizing a business

   A. Most businesses are large and complex enough to require departmentalization into subunits or departments to improve managerial efficiency.

   B. Departments may be classified as:

      1. Productive departments

         a. In a manufacturing business, departments engaged directly in manufacturing operations.
         b. In a merchandising business, departments that make sales.

      2. Service departments—support the activities of productive departments.

   C. Information to evaluate departments

      1. Cost centers—evaluated on the basis of their ability to control costs.
      2. Profit centers—evaluated on the basis of their ability to generate earnings.

V. Securing departmental information

   A. Separate sales accounts or sales analysis sheets may be used.

B. Departmental expenses

    1. Direct expenses are easily traced to specific departments.
    2. Indirect expenses must be allocated to the departments benefiting from them.
    3. The basis for allocating each expense should be a reasonable method of estimating the relative benefit gained by each department.
    4. The total costs charged to each service department should be reallocated to productive departments.

VI. Departmental contributions to overhead

    A. Calculated as revenues less direct costs and expenses.
    B. May be a better basis for evaluating profit centers when the allocation of indirect expenses are highly subjective.

VII. Eliminating an unprofitable department

    A. Neither net income nor contributions to overhead provides the best information on which to base a decision.
    B. A department should be eliminated only if its net loss exceeds its inescapable expenses.

VIII. Controllable costs and expenses

    A. Costs for which a manager has the power to determine or strongly influence amounts to be expended.
    B. Used to evaluate the performance of a manager.
    C. Provide the basis for a system of responsibility accounting.

IX. Responsibility accounting

    A. Each manager is held responsible for the costs and expenses that fall under the manager's control.
    B. Performance reports compare actual costs and expenses to budgeted amounts and are used to evaluate the effectiveness of each manager.
    C. A responsibility accounting system must reflect the fact that control over costs and expenses applies to several levels of management.

X. Joint costs—costs incurred to secure two or more essentially different products.

Part I

Many of the important ideas and concepts discussed in Chapter 23 are reflected in the following list of key terms. Test your understanding of these terms by matching the appropriate definitions with the terms. Record the number identifying the most appropriate definition in the blank space next to each term.

_____ Common expenses

_____ Controllable costs or expenses

_____ Cost center

_____ Departmental accounting

_____ Departmental contribution to overhead

_____ Direct costs or expenses

_____ Direct expenses

_____ Escapable expenses

_____ Indirect costs or expenses

_____ Indirect expenses

_____ Inescapable expenses

_____ Joint cost

_____ Performance report

_____ Productive departments

_____ Profit center

_____ Responsibility accounting

_____ Responsibility accounting budget

_____ Segmental reporting

_____ Service departments

_____ Uncontrollable cost

1. A financial report that compares actual costs and expenses to the budgeted amounts.

2. A unit of a business that incurs costs or expenses but does not directly generate revenues; as a result, a unit the efficiency of which cannot be judged in terms of its ability to generate earnings.

3. Departments that do not manufacture products or produce revenue but that supply other departments with essential services.

4. Accounting for the "parts" or subunits of a business, especially relating to the development of subunit information for the use of internal managers.

5. Expenses that are not easily associated with a specific, nonmanufacturing department.

6. Providing information about the subunits of a business, especially published information about a company's operations in different industries or geographical areas.

7. Expenses that would end with an unprofitable department's elimination.

8. Expenses that are easily associated with and assigned to a specific nonmanufacturing department.

9. Costs or expenses that are not easily traced to a cost object, such as a department; for example, costs incurred for the joint benefit of more than one department.

10. The amount by which a department's revenues exceed its direct costs and expenses.

11. A cost the amount of which a specific manager cannot control within a given period of time.

12. Those expenses of a business that benefit more than one segment of the business.

13. An accounting system designed to accumulate controllable costs in timely reports to be given to each manager determined responsible for the costs, and also to be used in judging the performance of each manager.

14. A single cost incurred to secure two or more essentially different products.

15. Costs or expenses that are easily traced to or associated with a cost object; for example, the cost of materials that become part of a manufactured product, or labor cost that is used solely in one processing department of a manufacturer, or wages expense incurred solely for the benefit of a specific department of a merchandising company.

16. Expenses that would continue even though a department were eliminated.

17. A unit of a business that incurs costs and generates revenues, the efficiency of which therefore can be judged in terms of its ability to generate earnings.

18. A plan that specifies the expected costs and expenses falling under the control of a manager.

19. Subunits of a business, the operations of which involve manufacturing or selling the goods or services of the business.

20. Costs over which the manager has the power to determine or strongly influence amounts to be expended.

Part II

Complete the following by filling in the blanks.

1. A departmental expense allocation sheet is used to allocate _____ expenses to all departments and also to allocate the _____ department expenses to the productive departments.

2. In responsibility accounting each manager is held responsible for the _____ _____ that fall under the manager's control.

3. Service department expenses are in effect _____ _____ of the selling or productive departments and therefore should be allocated to these departments.

4. An examination of controllable costs may be a better way to appraise a department manager's efficiency than an evaluation of the department's net income or its contribution to overhead because _____ _____ _____ _____ _____ .

5. Direct expenses can be identified easily with specific departments; but in the calculation of departmental net incomes, indirect expenses must be allocated on some _____ _____ basis.

6. A department's contribution to overhead is the amount its revenues _____ _____ .

7. When a concern goes beyond the calculation of departmental gross incomes and attempts to calculate net incomes by departments, an allocation of _____ _____ is required.

8. Unless it is continued because it brings business to other departments, it is usually wise to discontinue an unprofitable department when its losses exceed its _____ _____ .

9. A _____ center is a unit of the business that incurs costs but does not directly generate revenues, while a _____ center not only incurs costs but also generates revenues.

10. Some expenses of a department may be escaped by eliminating the department, but a(n) _____ will continue even though the department is discontinued.

120

11. In departmental accounting two different kinds of departments are recognized. One is engaged directly in the production of a product or in making sales and is called a

_____ department. The other kind is called a

_____ department because each performs some service for the productive departments.

12. Fifteen feet of Product X costing $12.00 per foot produce 5 feet of Product Y which sell for $50 per foot and 10 feet of Product Z which sell for $15 per foot. If the $180 cost of the 15 feet of Product X is allocated to Products Y and Z in the ratio of their market values, Product

Y should bear $ _____ of the cost and Product Z should bear

$ _____ .

13. Departmental information is used by management in _____

operations, _____ performances, allocating

resources, and in taking remedial _____ , but is generally not for publication.

14. The usual method for allocating a joint cost among several products is the ratio of __

_____

_____ .

15. In a system of responsibility accounting performance reports compare _____

_____ with _____

_____ .

Part III

The following statements are either true or false. Place your answer in the blank space that precedes each question.

_____ 1. Controllable costs and expenses are not the same thing as direct costs and expenses.

_____ 2. The costs of service departments are direct expenses of the selling departments to which they supply services.

_____ 3. When management considers eliminating a department, management should compare the department's net income with its escapable expenses.

_____ 4. An employee's wages may be either a direct or an indirect expense.

_____ 5. The term segmental reporting usually relates to information on the subunits of a business that is prepared for the use of internal managers.

_____ 6. A responsibility accounting budget is a financial report that compares actual costs and expenses to the budgeted amounts.

_____ 7. Direct expenses do not require allocation.

121

Part I

Part II

1. indirect, service

2. costs and expenses

3. indirect expenses

4. controllable costs and expenses are under the control of the manager and some of the factors that enter into net income and contribution to overhead are not

5. fair

6. exceed its direct costs and expenses

7. indirect expenses

8. inescapable expenses

9. cost, profit

10. inescapable expense

11. productive, service

12. Product Y, $112.50; Product Z, $67.50

13. controlling, appraising, actions

14. the market values of the joint products at the point of separation

15. actual costs and expenses, budgeted costs and expenses

Part III

1. True
2. False
3. False
4. True
5. False
6. False
7. True

24

Cost-Volume-Profit Analysis

Your objectives in studying this chapter should include learning how to:

Describe the different types of cost behavior experienced by a typical company.

State the assumptions that underlie cost-volume-profit analysis and explain how these assumptions restrict the usefulness of the information obtained from the analysis.

Prepare and interpret a scatter diagram of past costs and sales volume.

Calculate a break-even point for a single product company and graphically plot its costs and revenues.

Describe some extensions that may be added to the basic cost-volume-profit analysis of break-even point.

Calculate a composite sales unit for a multiproduct company and a break-even point for such a company.

Define or explain the words and phrases listed in the chapter Glossary.

Topical Outline

I. Cost-volume-profit analysis

   A. A means of predicting the effect of changes in costs and sales levels on the income of a business.
   B. Often called break-even analysis—because it involves the determination of the sales level at which a company neither earns a profit nor incurs a loss (the point at which it breaks even).

II. Cost behavior

   A. Fixed cost—remains unchanged in total amount over a wide range of production levels.
   B. Variable cost—total amount changes proportionately with production level changes.
   C. Semivariable cost—changes with production level changes, but not proportionately.
   D. Stair-step cost—remains constant over a given range of production, then increases by a lump sum if production goes higher, then remains constant for another range of production.

III. Cost assumptions

   A. If a cost-volume-profit analysis is to be reliable, the following assumptions must be reasonably accurate:

      1. Per unit selling price must be constant.
      2. Costs classified as "variable" must, in fact, behave as variable costs.
      3. Costs classified as "fixed" must, in fact, remain constant over wide changes in the level of production.

   B. These assumptions tend to provide reliable analyses because:

      1. Even if individual variable (or fixed) costs do not act in a truly variable (or fixed) manner, aggregating such costs may offset such violations of the assumption.
      2. The assumptions are intended to apply only over the relevant range of operations.

IV. Estimating cost behavior

   A. Mixed cost—a cost that includes two components, one of which is fixed and one of which is variable.
   B. Scatter diagram—a graph used to display the relationship between costs and volume in which the cost and volume for each period is shown as a point on the diagram.
   C. Estimated line of cost behavior—attempts to reflect the average relationship between total costs and sales volume.

      1. A crude means of deriving this line is the high-low method.
      2. A visual placement of the estimated line of cost behavior on a scatter diagram is often a better method.
      3. A more sophisticated method is the statistical method of least-squares regression.

V. Break-even analysis

   A. Break-even point—the sales level at which a company neither earns a profit nor incurs a loss.

   B. Break-even point in units $= \dfrac{\text{Fixed costs}}{\text{Contribution margin per unit}}$

   C. Break-even point in dollars $= \dfrac{\text{Fixed costs}}{\text{Contribution rate}}$

D. Contribution margin per unit = Sales price − Variable costs per unit.

E. Contribution rate = Contribution margin per unit expressed as a percentage of sales price.

F. A cost-volume-profit analysis may be shown graphically in a break-even graph.

VI. Extensions of the break-even calculation concept

A. Sales required for a desired net income

$$\text{Sales at desired income level} = \frac{\text{Fixed costs} + \text{Net income} + \text{Income taxes}}{\text{Contribution rate}}$$

B. Margin of safety

$$\text{Margin of safety} = \frac{\text{Sales} - \text{Break-even sales}}{\text{Sales}}$$

C. Income from a given sales level

Income = Sales − (Fixed costs + Variable costs)

VII. Multiproduct break-even point

A. A composite unit is a hypothetical unit made up of the units of each product in their expected sales mix.

B. Break-even point in composite units $= \dfrac{\text{Fixed costs}}{\text{Composite contribution margin per unit}}$

Part I

Many of the important ideas and concepts discussed in Chapter 24 are reflected in the following list of key terms. Test your understanding of these terms by matching the appropriate definitions with the terms. Record the number identifying the most appropriate definition in the blank space next to each term.

_____ Break-even analysis   _____ Margin of safety

_____ Break-even point   _____ Mixed cost

_____ Contribution margin per unit   _____ Relevant range of operations

_____ Contribution rate   _____ Sales mix

_____ Cost-volume-profit analysis   _____ Scatter diagram

_____ Estimated line of cost behavior   _____ Semivariable cost

_____ Fixed cost   _____ Stair-step cost

_____ High-low method   _____ Variable cost

_____ Least-squares regression

1. A cost that includes two components, one of which is fixed and one of which is variable.

2. A crude technique for deriving an estimated line of cost behavior, according to which the highest and lowest costs shown on a scatter diagram are connected with a straight line.

3. The ratio in which a company's different products are sold.

4. A synonym for cost-volume-profit analysis.

5. A cost that changes with production volume but not in the same proportion.

6. A sophisticated method of deriving an estimated line of cost behavior; the resulting estimate can be described as a line that best fits the actual cost and volume data of a company.

7. A cost that changes in total amount proportionately with production level changes.

8. The amount by which a company's current sales exceed the sales necessary to break even.

9. A method of predicting the effects of changes in costs and sales level on the income of a business.

10. The dollar amount that the sale of one unit contributes toward recovery of fixed costs and then toward a profit.

11. A cost that remains unchanged in total amount over a wide range of production levels.

12. A graph used to display the relationship between costs and volume in which the cost and volume for each period is shown as a point on the diagram.

13. The contribution margin per unit expressed as a percentage of sales price.

14. A cost that remains constant over a range of production, then increases by a lump sum if production is expanded beyond this range, then remains constant over another range of production increases, and so forth.

15. A line that attempts to reflect the average relationship between cost and volume.

16. The sales level at which a company neither earns a profit nor incurs a loss.

17. The normal operating range for a business, which excludes extremely high and low levels of production that are not apt to be encountered.

Part II

Complete the following by filling in the blanks.

1. The _____ (total, per unit) amount of a variable cost changes with production volume and in the same proportion. A typical example of a variable cost is _____ .

2. A fixed cost remains _____ at all levels of production within the relevant range; however, fixed costs per unit of product produced decrease as the number of units _____ . A typical example of a fixed cost is _____ .

3. The _____ method of deriving an estimated line of cost behavior results in an approximation that can be described as a line that best fits the actual cost and sales volume experience of the company.

4. An obvious deficiency of the high-low method of deriving an estimated line of cost behavior is that _____
_____
_____
_____ .

5. In preparing a scatter diagram of costs and volume, _____
_____ normally is measured on the horizontal axis and _____ normally is measured on the vertical axis.

6. When lumped together, a number of variable costs that are not truly variable often tend to _____ each other and can therefore be plotted as a straight line in a cost-volume-profit analysis.

7. When the selling price per unit of product is not constant, or variable costs are not truly variable, or fixed costs are not truly fixed, the results of a cost-volume-profit analysis will not be _____ .

8. Conventional cost-volume-profit analysis is based on relationships that can be expressed as straight lines. Straight lines result when:
   a. _____ ,
   b. _____ ,
   c. _____ .

9. Semivariable costs vary with volume but not in the same _____
_____ .

Part III

A company incurs $60,000 of annual fixed costs in manufacturing and selling a product that it sells for $15 per unit. The variable costs of manufacturing and selling the product are $9 per unit.

1. The contribution margin on each unit of product sold is $ _____ .

2. The contribution rate on the product is:

$$\frac{\text{Contribution Margin, \$ \underline{\hspace{3cm}}}}{\text{Selling Price per Unit, \$ \underline{\hspace{3cm}}}} \times 100 = \underline{\hspace{3cm}} \%$$

3. The break-even point in units is:

$$\frac{\text{Fixed Costs, \$ \underline{\hspace{3cm}}}}{\text{Contribution Margin, \$ \underline{\hspace{3cm}}}} = \underline{\hspace{3cm}} \text{ Units}$$

4. The break-even point in dollars is:

$$\frac{\text{Fixed Costs, \$ \underline{\hspace{3cm}}}}{\text{Contribution Rate, \underline{\hspace{3cm}} \%}} = \$ \underline{\hspace{3cm}}$$

5. Assume a 30% income tax rate, and present below the formula and the calculation of the sales volume in dollars this company must achieve to earn a $35,000 annual after-tax net income.

6. Assume a 30% income tax rate, and calculate below the after-tax income the company will earn from a $420,000 sales volume.

Part I

Part II

1. total, direct material costs

2. the same or unchanged, increases, rent or property taxes

3. least-squares regression

4. it totally ignores all of the available cost and sales volume points except the highest and the lowest

5. volume in dollars or units, cost

6. offset

7. reliable

8. a. The per unit selling price is constant
    b. Variable costs are truly variable
    c. Fixed costs are truly fixed

9. proportion

Part III

1. $6

2. $$\frac{\text{Contribution Margin, \$6}}{\text{Selling Price per Unit, \$15}} = 40\%$$

3. $$\frac{\text{Fixed Costs, \$60,000}}{\text{Contribution Margin, \$6}} = 10{,}000 \text{ Units}$$

4. $$\frac{\text{Fixed Costs, \$60,000}}{\text{Contribution Rate, 40\%}} = \$150{,}000$$

5. $$\frac{\text{Fixed Costs, } \$60{,}000 + \text{Net Income, } \$35{,}000 + \text{Income Taxes, } \$15{,}000}{\text{Contribution Rate, } 40\%} = \$275{,}000$$

6. Variable costs are 60% of sales.

   Before-Tax Income = Sales - [Fixed Costs + (0.6 × Sales)]

   Before-Tax Income = $420,000 - [$60,000 + (0.6 × $420,000)] = $108,000

   After-Tax Income = $108,000 × 70% = $75,600

25

The Master Budget: A Formal Plan for the Business

Your objectives in studying this chapter should include learning how to:

Explain the importance of budgeting.

Describe the specific benefits derived from budgeting.

List the sequence of steps required to prepare a master budget.

Prepare each budget in a master budget and explain the importance of each budget to the overall budgeting process.

Integrate the individual budgets into planned financial statements.

Define or explain the words and phrases listed in the chapter Glossary.

Topical Outline

I. The budgeting process

    A. Budgeting is a process of preparing a formal statement of future plans.

        1. A master budget is a comprehensive or overall plan for the business.
        2. Rolling budgets involve a series of revised budgets that are prepared in the practice of continuous budgeting.

    B. Benefits from budgeting

        1. Promotes study, research, and a focus on the future.
        2. Provides a basis for evaluating performance.
        3. Provides a means of coordinating the subunits of a business.
        4. Provides a system of communicating management's plans for the business.
        5. Provides a source of motivation for employees.

    C. Budget committee—should include representatives from the various subunits of the business that are affected by the budget.
    D. The budget period

        1. Normally coincides with the accounting period.
        2. For long-range plans, may involve five to ten years in the future.

II. The master budget typically includes:

    A. Operating budgets

        1. Sales budget
        2. For merchandising companies, a merchandise purchases budget
        3. For manufacturing companies:

            a. Production budget
            b. Manufacturing budget

        4. Selling expense budget
        5. General and administrative expense budget

    B. Capital expenditures budget
    C. Financial budgets

        1. Budgeted statement of cash receipts and cash disbursements (called the cash budget)
        2. Budgeted income statement
        3. Budgeted balance sheet

III. Preparing the master budget

    A. The sales budget must be prepared first.
    B. The remaining operating budgets are prepared next.
    C. The capital expenditures budget is prepared next.
    D. The budgeted statement of cash receipts and disbursements (the cash budget) is prepared next.
    E. The budgeted income statement is prepared next.
    F. Finally, the budgeted balance sheet is prepared.

Part I

Many of the important ideas and concepts discussed in Chapter 25 are reflected in the following list of key terms. Test your understanding of these terms by matching the appropriate definitions with the terms. Record the number identifying the most appropriate definition in the blank space next to each term.

_____ Budget

_____ Budgeted balance sheet

_____ Budgeted income statement

_____ Budgeting

_____ Capital expenditures budget

_____ Cash budget

_____ Continuous budgeting

_____ Manufacturing budget

_____ Master budget

_____ Merchandise purchases budget

_____ Production budget

_____ Rolling budgets

_____ Sales budget

1. A comprehensive or overall plan for the business that typically includes budgets for sales, expenses, production, capital expenditures, cash, and also a planned income statement and balance sheet.

2. A projected balance sheet estimated to result at the end of the future budgeting period if the activities projected in each of the related budgets actually occur.

3. An estimate of goods to be sold and revenue to be derived from sales; serves as the usual starting point in the budgeting procedure.

4. A formal statement of future plans, usually expressed in monetary terms.

5. A sequence of revised budgets that are prepared in the practice of continuous budgeting.

6. A projected income statement that draws upon the estimates shown in all of the related revenue and expense budgets and shows the effects of the separate budgets on the income of the future budget period.

7. A statement of the estimated costs for raw materials, direct labor, and manufacturing overhead associated with producing the number of units estimated in the production budget.

8. An estimate of the number of units to be produced during a budget period, based on the budgeted sales for the period and the levels of inventory necessary to support future sales.

9. A forecast of cash receipts and disbursements.

10. An estimate of the units and/or cost of merchandise to be purchased by a merchandising company.

11. A listing of the plant and equipment to be purchased if the proposed production program is carried out. Also called the plant and equipment budget.

12. The process of planning future business actions and expressing those plans in a formal manner.

13. The practice of preparing budgets for each of several future periods and revising those budgets each period, adding a new budget each time so that budgets are always available for a given number of future periods.

Part II

Complete the following by filling in the blanks.

1. When a budget committee returns a budget to a department for reconsideration and the department adjusts the budgeted amounts, it is especially important for all parties to agree

   that the budget figures are _____ .

2. Central guidance in preparing a master budget is provided by the _____ _____ , which is made up of _____ _____ who are responsible for seeing that budget figures are realistically established and coordinated.

3. Benefits to be obtained from budgeting include:

   a. _____
   _____ .

   b. _____
   _____ .

   c. _____
   _____ .

   d. _____
   _____ .

   e. _____
   _____ .

4. Long-range budgets of two, three, five, and ten years should reflect _____ _____ . These budgets are particularly important in planning for _____ _____ .

5. The first budget to be prepared in the process of developing a master budget is the _____ ; the last statement or budget to be prepared in the sequence is the _____ _____ .

6. The three types of budgets included in a master budget are:

   a. _____ .
   b. _____ .
   c. _____ .

7. The practice of revising the entire set of budgets as each monthly or quarterly budget period goes by, adding new budgets to replace those that have elapsed, thus maintaining budgets for a full year in advance, is called _____ . The budgets resulting from this process are called _____ .

8. A master budget is _____
   _____ .

9. A budget is _____
   _____ .

10. Budgeting is the process of _____
   _____
   _____ .

11. A company's potential need for short-term loans would be discovered in the process of preparing a _____ .

12. Planned purchases of new plant and equipment are disclosed in the _____ _____ .

13. A budget that is used only by merchandising companies is the _____ _____ ; manufacturing companies, on the other hand, are unique in their use of _____ and _____ .

Part I

Part II

1. reasonable and attainable

2. budget committee, department heads or other high-level executives

3. a. Good decision-making processes based on research, study, and a focus on the future

   b. A superior basis for evaluating performance and a more effective control mechanism
   c. A system of coordinating business activities
   d. A means of communicating management's plans to the organization
   e. A means of motivating people

4. the planned accomplishment of long-range objectives, major expenditures of capital to buy plant and equipment

5. sales budget, budgeted balance sheet

6. a. Operating budgets

   b. Capital expenditures budget
   c. Financial budgets

7. continuous budgeting, rolling budgets

8. a comprehensive or overall plan for the business

9. a formal statement of future plans

10. planning future business actions and expressing those plans in a formal manner

11. cash budget

12. capital expenditures budget

13. merchandise purchases budget; production budgets, manufacturing budgets

26

Flexible Budgets; Standard Costs

Your objectives in studying this chapter should include learning how to:

State the deficiencies of fixed budgets.

Prepare flexible budgets and state their advantages.

State what standard costs represent, how they are determined, and how they are used in the evaluation process.

Calculate material, labor, and overhead variances, and state what each variance indicates about the performance of a company.

Explain the relevance of standard cost accounting to the management philosophy known as "management by exception."

Define or explain the words and phrases listed in the chapter Glossary.

Topical Outline

I. Fixed budgets and performance reports

    A. A fixed or static budget is based on a single estimate of sales or production volume.

    B. Comparisons between actual and budgeted amounts are presented in a performance report.

        1. Differences between actual and budgeted amounts are called variances.

        2. In a fixed budget performance report, reported variances may result from activity levels being different from budgeted amounts and also from unexpected levels of efficiency or inefficiency.

II. Flexible budgets

    A. Each type of cost is classified as a variable cost or as a fixed cost.

        1. Each variable cost is expressed as a constant amount of cost per unit of sales (or per sales dollar).

        2. Fixed costs are budgeted in terms of the total amount of each fixed cost that is expected regardless of the sales volume that may occur within the relevant range.

    B. A flexible budget performance report is designed to analyze the difference between actual performance and budgeted performance, given the actual level of operations.

III. Standard costs and variance analysis

    A. One variation of the two basic types of manufacturing systems (job order and process) is a standard cost system.

        1. Standard costs are, in effect, budgeted costs.

        2. Variances are differences between actual costs and standard costs.

    B. Material and labor variances

        1. Cost variance = quantity variance ± price variance.

        2. Quantity variance = (actual units − standard units) × standard price.

        3. Price variance = (actual price − standard price) × actual units.

    C. Overhead variances

        1. Volume variance = budgeted overhead at the actual operating level less the standard overhead charged to production.

        2. Controllable variance = overhead actually incurred less overhead budgeted at the operating level achieved.

        3. The volume and controllable variances may be combined to account for the difference between overhead actually incurred and overhead charged to production.

    D. Use of standard costs and variance analysis focuses management's attention on irregular performance and follows the principle of management by exception.

    E. Standard costs may be recorded in the accounts or used in analyses that are not entered in the accounts.

Many of the important ideas and concepts discussed in Chapter 26 are reflected in the following list of key terms. Test your understanding of these terms by matching the appropriate definitions with the terms. Record the number identifying the most appropriate definition in the blank space next to each term.

_____ Controllable variance   _____ Price variance

_____ Cost variance   _____ Quantity variance

_____ Fixed budget   _____ Standard costs

_____ Flexible budget   _____ Static budget

_____ Flexible budget performance report   _____ Variable budget

_____ Management by exception   _____ Volume variance

_____ Performance report

1. A synonym for fixed budget.

2. A technique whereby management gives its attention to the variances in which actual costs are significantly different from standard costs and generally ignores the cost situations in which performance is satisfactory.

3. The difference between actual cost and budgeted cost that was caused by a difference between the actual number of units used and the number of units budgeted.

4. A financial report that compares actual cost and/or revenue performance with budgeted amounts and designates the differences between them as favorable or unfavorable variances.

5. The difference between the overhead actually incurred and the overhead budgeted at the operating level achieved.

6. The difference between the amount of overhead budgeted at the actual operating level achieved during the period and the standard amount of overhead charged to production during the period.

7. A budget based on a single estimate of sales or production volume that gives no consideration to the possibility that the actual sales or production volume may differ from the assumed amount.

8. The costs that should be incurred under normal conditions in producing a given product or part or in performing a particular service.

9. A difference between actual and budgeted revenue or cost caused by the actual price per unit being different from the budgeted price per unit.

10. A report designed to analyze the difference between actual performance and budgeted performance, where the budgeted amounts are based on the actual sales volume or level of activity.

11. A synonym for flexible budget.

12. The difference between the actual or incurred amount of a cost and the standard or budgeted amount of the cost.

13. A budget that provides budgeted amounts for all levels of production within the relevant range.

Part II

Complete the following by filling in the blanks.

1. Standard costs are the costs that _____ be incurred under normal conditions to produce a given product, part, or service; and they are used to judge _____ incurred when the product or service is produced. Standard costs are also used to place responsibilities when _____ _____ vary from standard.

2. A standard cost system is one based on standard or _____ costs.

3. In analyzing the total variance in a cost such as direct materials, the portion that is caused by a difference between the actual price per unit and the budgeted price per unit is called a _____ . The portion caused by a difference between the actual number of units used and the budgeted number of units to be used is called a _____ .

4. A flexible budget performance report is designed to analyze _____ _____ _____ where the budgeted amounts are based on the _____ sales volume or level of activity.

5. A volume variance results when the operating level of a factory varies from the standard or _____ operating level.

6. When overhead costs vary from standard, the variance may be divided into a _____ _____ variance and a _____ variance.

7. In preparing a flexible budget each _____ cost is expressed as a constant amount of cost per unit of sales (or per sales dollar). Each _____ cost is budgeted in terms of the total amount that is expected to be incurred.

8. Preparation of a flexible budget requires that each type of cost be analyzed and classified as either _____ or _____ .

9. Budgets that recognize the fact that different levels of activity should produce different amounts of cost are called _____ or _____ _____ budgets.

10. A budget that is based on a single estimate of sales volume is called a _____ _____ or _____ budget.

11. A variable budget is used in establishing standard overhead costs because when actual costs are known, they should be compared with the standards of the production level actually _____ and not with those of some other "hoped for" level.

12. A _____ or variable factory overhead budget is the starting point in establishing reasonable standards for overhead costs.

13. When actual costs vary from standard costs, the difference is called a _____ _____ , and may be either favorable or unfavorable. A _____ is favorable when actual costs are _____ (below, above) the standard.

14. Standard costs are established by means of accounting, engineering, personnel, and other studies made _____ (before, after) the product, part, or service is produced.

15. When management by exception is practiced, management gives its attention only to variances in which actual costs are significantly different from _____ _____ and ignores situations in which performance is _____ _____ .

16. Control of a business is gained by _____ the actions of the people who are responsible for its revenues, costs, and expenses; and when a standard cost system is in use, control is maintained by taking appropriate actions when _____ _____ vary from standard.

Part III

A company purchased 784 pounds of material for $11,446.40 and used the material to produce 2,900 units of product. The standards for this material are 0.25 pounds of material per unit of product at $15 per pound. Calculate the material price, quantity, and cost variances related to this situation.

Price variance:

_____ (Actual units) × _____ (Actual price) = $ _____
_____ (Actual units) × _____ (Std. price) = _____
Price variance _____ (favorable or unfavorable) = $ _____

Quantity variance:

_____ (Actual units) × _____ (Std. price) = $ _____
_____ (Std. units) × _____ (Std. price) = _____
Quantity variance _____ (favorable or unfavorable) = $ _____

Cost variance:

_____ (Actual units) × _____ (Actual price) = $ _____
_____ (Std. units) × _____ (Std. price) = _____
Cost variance _____ (favorable or unfavorable) = $ _____

Part IV

A company operated at 78% of capacity, producing 6,240 units of product, and incurring $22,776 of overhead costs. The company was budgeted to operate at 85% of capacity, which would have produced 6,800 units of product. Budgeted overhead at 85% of capacity is $23,800, consisting of $10,200 variable cost and $13,600 fixed cost. Calculate answers to the following questions.

(a) What was the predetermined standard overhead rate (per unit of product)?

$$\frac{\$ \underline{\hspace{2cm}} \text{ budgeted overhead at 85\% capacity}}{\underline{\hspace{2cm}} \text{ units of production at 85\% capacity}} = \$ \underline{\hspace{2cm}} \text{ per unit}$$

(b) What was the budgeted variable overhead cost per unit?

$$\frac{\$ \underline{\hspace{2cm}} \text{ budgeted variable cost at 85\% capacity}}{\underline{\hspace{2cm}} \text{ units of production at 85\% capacity}} = \$ \underline{\hspace{2cm}} \text{ per unit}$$

(c) What amount of overhead was charged to production?

_____ units produced × _____ overhead rate   = $ _____

(d) On a flexible budget, what was the budgeted amount of overhead assuming a production level of 78% of capacity of 6,240 units?

$ _____ variable overhead per unit × 6,240 units .. = $ _____

Budgeted fixed overhead .... =   _____

Total budgeted overhead at 78% of capacity .... = $ _____

(e) What was the volume variance?

Budgeted overhead at 78% of capacity .... = $ _____
Standard overhead charged to production:

_____ std. overhead rate × 6,240 units produced ..... =   _____

Variance _____ (favorable or unfavorable) .... = $ _____

(f) What was the controllable variance?

Actual overhead incurred .... = $ _____

Overhead budgeted at operating level achieved .... =   _____

Variance _____ (favorable or unfavorable) .... = $ _____

Part I

Controllable variance	5	Price variance	9
Cost variance	12	Quantity variance	3
Fixed budget	7	Standard costs	8
Flexible budget	13	Static budget	1 (or 7)
Flexible budget performance report	10	Variable budget	11 (or 13)
Management by exception	2	Volume variance	6
Performance report	4		

Part II

1. should, the actual costs, actual costs
2. budgeted
3. price variance, quantity variance
4. the difference between actual performance and budgeted performance, actual
5. expected or normal
6. volume, controllable
7. variable, fixed
8. fixed, variable
9. flexible, variable
10. fixed, static
11. achieved
12. flexible
13. variance, variance, below
14. before
15. standard, normal
16. controlling, actual costs

Part III

Price variance:

784 (Actual units) × $14.60 (Actual price)	=	$11,446.40
784 (Actual units) × $15.00 (Std. price)	=	11,760.00
Price variance (favorable)	=	$ 313.60

Quantity variance:

784 (Actual units) × $15.00 (Std. price)	=	$11,760.00
725 (Std. units) × $15.00 (Std. price)	=	10,875.00
Quantity variance (unfavorable)	=	$ 885.00

Cost variance:

784 (Actual units) × $14.60 (Actual price)	=	$11,446.40
725 (Std. units) × $15.00 (Std. price)	=	10,875.00
Cost variance (unfavorable)	=	$ 571.40

Part IV

(a) Predetermined standard overhead rate (per unit of product):

$$\frac{\$23,800 \text{ budgeted overhead at 85\% capacity}}{6,800 \text{ units of production at 85\% capacity}} = \$3.50 \text{ per unit}$$

(b) Budgeted variable overhead cost per unit:

$$\frac{\$10,200 \text{ budgeted variable cost at 85\% capacity}}{6,800 \text{ units of production at 85\% capacity}} = \$1.50 \text{ per unit}$$

(c) Amount of overhead charged to production:

6,240 units produced × $3.50 overhead rate = $21,840

(d) Budgeted amount of overhead at 78% of capacity, or 6,240 units:

$1.50 variable overhead per unit × 6,240 units	=	$ 9,360
Budgeted fixed overhead	=	13,600
Total budgeted overhead at 78% of capacity	=	$22,960

(e) Volume variance:

Budgeted overhead at 78% of capacity	=	$22,960
Standard overhead charged to production:		
$3.50 std. overhead rate × 6,240 units produced	=	21,840
Variance (unfavorable)	=	$ 1,120

(f) Controllable variance:

Actual overhead incurred	=	$22,776
Overhead budgeted at operating level achieved	=	22,960
Variance (favorable)	=	$ 184

27

Capital Budgeting; Managerial Decisions

Your objectives in studying this chapter should include learning how to:

Describe the impact of capital budgeting on the operations of a company.

Calculate a payback period on an investment and state the inherent limitations of this method.

Calculate a rate of return on an investment and state the assumptions on which this method is based.

Describe the information obtained by a comparison of net present values, the procedures involved in using this method, and the problems associated with its use.

Explain the effects of incremental costs on a decision to accept or reject additional business and on a decision whether to make or buy a given product.

State the meaning of sunk costs, out-of-pocket costs, and opportunity costs, and describe the importance of each type of cost to decisions such as to scrap or rebuild defective units or to sell a product as is or process it further.

Define or explain the words and phrases listed in the chapter Glossary.

Topical Outline

I. Capital budgeting—planning plant asset investments

   A. Payback method of comparing investment opportunities

      1. $\text{Payback period in years} = \dfrac{\text{Cost of plant asset}}{\text{Annual net cash flow}}$

      2. This method fails to incorporate:

         a. Fluctuation in annual cash flows

         b. Length of time revenue will continue to be earned beyond the payback period

   B. Rate of return on average investment method

      1. $\text{Rate of return} = \dfrac{\text{After-tax net income}}{\text{Average investment}}$

      2. Calculation of average investment

         a. If sales are assumed to be earned evenly throughout the year so that the cost recovery from depreciation is assumed to occur at the middle of the year, average investment is the beginning book value plus any salvage value, divided by the number of years in the asset's life.

         b. If revenue is received at year-end and the cost recovery from depreciation is also at year-end, average investment is the average of the first and last year's beginning-of-year book values.

      3. This method fails to incorporate:

         a. Relative risk of alternative investments

         b. Fluctuation in annual cash flows

   C. Comparison of net present values

      1. All future cash flows are discounted at a rate of return deemed satisfactory by management.

      2. The cost to purchase is subtracted from the present value of future cash flows to determine net present value.

      3. A positive net present value implies a favorable investment.

II. Analysis of specific decisions

   A. Important cost concepts

      1. Sunk costs result from past irrevocable decisions and cannot be avoided.

      2. Out-of-pocket costs require a current (or future) outlay of funds.

      3. Opportunity costs are potential benefits lost as a result of choosing an alternative course of action.

   B. Accepting additional business

      1. Incremental (or differential) costs are the additional, relevant costs of accepting additional business.

      2. Sales from additional business should be compared to the incremental costs in deciding whether or not to accept the business.

   C. Scrap or rebuild defective units

      1. Previously incurred costs to manufacture the units are sunk costs and therefore irrelevant to the decision.

      2. If rebuilding the units uses production capacity that could have otherwise been employed at some net return, that return is an opportunity cost of rebuilding.

D. Process or sell

1. In evaluating the possibility of further processing, incremental costs and also revenue lost by not selling units as is must be subtracted from revenues from selling processed units.
2. Past manufacturing costs are sunk costs.

E. Deciding the sales mix

1. Production capacity should be allocated to products having the largest contribution margin.
2. If production capacity is limited, contribution margin must be expressed in terms of the amount of return derived from the capacity available.

Part I

Many of the important ideas and concepts discussed in Chapter 27 are reflected in the following list of key terms. Test your understanding of these terms by matching the appropriate definitions with the terms. Record the number identifying the most appropriate definition in the blank space next to each term.

_____ Capital budgeting   _____ Out-of-pocket cost

_____ Differential cost   _____ Payback period

_____ Incremental cost   _____ Rate of return on average investment

_____ Net present value   _____ Sunk cost

_____ Opportunity cost

1. A synonym for incremental cost.

2. The time required to recover the original cost of an investment through net cash flows from the investment.

3. The benefit of one course of action that is lost or sacrificed as a result of choosing an alternative course of action.

4. A cost requiring a current outlay of funds.

5. Planning plant asset investments; involves the preparation of cost and revenue estimates for all proposed projects, an examination of the merits of each, and a choice of those worthy of investment.

6. A cost incurred as a consequence of a past irrevocable decision and that, therefore, cannot be avoided; hence, irrelevant to decisions affecting the future.

7. The value of an investment calculated by discounting the future cash flows from the investment at an interest rate that gives a satisfactory return on investment and then subtracting the present cost of the investment.

8. The annual after-tax income from the sale of an asset's product divided by the average investment in the asset.

9. An additional cost resulting from a particular course of action.

Part II

Complete the following by filling in the blanks.

1. A short payback period should not be the only factor considered in choosing between investment opportunities because the payback period ignores _____

_____

_____ .

2. A short payback period is desirable in an investment because the sooner an investment is recovered the sooner the funds are _____

_____ , and a short payback period also means a short _____ period.

3. The annual net cash flow from the sale of a machine's product includes the net income earned from the sale of the product plus the annual _____ on the machine.

4. Planning plant asset investments is called _____ .

    5. An opportunity cost is a _____ that is lost as a result of _____ .

      Opportunity costs _____ (are, are not) entered in the accounting records.

6. An out-of-pocket cost is a cost _____
_____ .

7. A sunk cost is a cost resulting from _____
_____ .

8. The incremental or differential costs of accepting an additional volume of business are the _____ costs.

9. In choosing between investment opportunities, an investment with a _____ net present value normally should be rejected; and in choosing between two investments that are otherwise equal, the one with the _____ positive net present value usually is the better.

10. It is impossible to say that the return on an investment is either good or bad without relating the return to _____ returns.

Part III

A company is about to purchase a new machine that will cost $45,000, have a three-year life and no salvage value, and be depreciated on a straight-line basis. Revenues and cost recovery of depreciation are assumed to occur near the end of each year. The company expects to sell the product of the machine during each of the next three years with these annual results:

Sales		$195,000
Costs:		
Materials, labor, and overhead other than depreciation on the new machine	$108,000	
Depreciation on the new machine	15,000	
Selling and administrative expenses	60,000	183,000
Operating income		$ 12,000
Income taxes		4,800
Net income		$ 7,200

1. The investment in this machine will produce an annual net cash flow of $ _____ .

2. The payback period on this machine is:

$$\frac{\text{Cost of Machine, \$ _____}}{\text{Annual Net Cash Flow, \$ _____}} = \text{_____ Years}$$

3. The average investment in this machine is:

$$\frac{\text{Book Value First Year, \$ _____ + Book Value Last Year, \$ _____}}{2} = \text{\$ _____}$$

4. The rate of return on the average investment in this machine is:

Net Income from
Sales of Product, $ _____
———————————————— × 100 = _____ %
Average
Investment, $ _____

5. If the company demands a 10% compound return on capital investments, the net present value of the cash flows from this machine discounted at 10% are:

Present value of the cash flows (2.4869 × $ _____) ...... $ _____

Amount to be invested .... _____

Positive net present value .... $ _____

159

Part I

Capital budgeting 5

Differential cost .... 1 (or 9)

Incremental cost 9

Net present value 7

Opportunity cost 3

Out-of-pocket cost 4

Payback period 2

Rate of return on average investment 8

Sunk cost 6

Part II

1. the length of time cash will be generated after the end of the payback period as well as fluctuations in the annual cash flows

2. available for other uses, "bail-out"

3. depreciation

4. capital budgeting

5. potential benefit, choosing an alternative course of action, are not

6. requiring a current outlay of funds

7. a past irrevocable decision

8. additional

9. negative, higher

10. other

Part III

1. $22,200

2. $$\frac{\text{Cost of Machine, \$45,000}}{\text{Annual Net Cash Flow, \$22,200}} = 2.03 \text{ Years}$$

3. $$\frac{\begin{array}{l}\text{Book Value} \\ \text{First Year, \$45,000}\end{array} + \begin{array}{l}\text{Book Value} \\ \text{Last Year, \$15,000}\end{array}}{2} = \$30,000$$

4. $$\frac{\begin{array}{l}\text{Net Income from} \\ \text{Sales of Product, \$7,200}\end{array}}{\begin{array}{l}\text{Average} \\ \text{Investment, \$30,000}\end{array}} \times 100 = 24\%$$

5.
Present value of the cash flows (2.4869 × $22,200)	$55,209
Amount to be invested	45,000
Positive net present value	$10,209

28

Tax Considerations in Business Decisions

Your objectives in studying this chapter should include learning how to:

Explain the importance of tax planning.

Describe the steps an individual must go through to calculate his or her tax liability; and explain the difference between deductions to arrive at adjusted gross income, deductions from adjusted gross income, and tax credits.

Calculate the taxable income and net tax liability for an individual.

Define capital assets and describe the tax treatment for capital losses in comparison with ordinary (non-capital) losses.

Describe the differences between the calculations of taxable income and tax liability for corporations and for individuals.

Explain why income tax expenses shown in financial statements may differ from taxes actually payable.

Define or explain the words and phrases listed in the chapter Glossary.

I. Tax planning

   A. Designing business transactions to provide the minimum tax under the law is legitimate tax avoidance.

   B. Concealing legal tax liabilities is tax evasion.

   C. Tax planning should take into consideration all forms of tax, not simply federal income tax.

II. Federal income tax

   A. Is intended to accomplish a variety of social objectives.

   B. Tax Reform Act of 1986 was designed to:

      1. Broaden the tax base (through the repeal of or reduction in many tax deductions).

      2. Reduce tax rates.

      3. Make the income tax more neutral.

   C. Applies to three different classes of taxpayers:

      1. Individuals.

      2. Corporations.

      3. Estates and trusts.

III. Individual income tax

   A. Typical calculation of taxable income is:

Gross income
   Less: Deductions to arrive at adjusted gross income
_____

Adjusted gross income
   Less: The greater of total itemized deductions or the standard deduction.
        Deduction for exemptions.
_____

Taxable income
_____

   B. Gross income—all income from whatever source derived, unless expressly excluded from taxation by law; excluded are:

      1. Gifts.

      2. Inheritances.

      3. Scholarships (up to the cost of tuition, fees, and course-related materials).

      4. Social security benefits.

      5. Veterans' benefits.

      6. Workmen's compensation insurance.

      7. Usually, proceeds of life insurance policies paid upon the death of the insured.

      8. Interest on the obligations of states and their subdivisions.

   C. Deductions to arrive at adjusted gross income include:

      1. Ordinary and necessary expenses of a self-employed person in carrying on a business, trade, or profession.

      2. Expenses of producing rent income.

   D. Deductions from adjusted gross income

      1. The greater of itemized deductions or the standard deduction.

      2. A deduction for each exemption.

   E. Federal income tax rates

      1. Are progressive in nature.

      2. Are contained in Tax Rate Schedules or in simplified Tax Tables for those who qualify.

F. Tax credits may include:

1. Credit for the elderly.
2. Foreign tax credit.
3. Earned income credit.

G. Special treatment of capital gains and losses

1. Deductions of capital losses are limited to the amount of capital gains plus $3,000 ($1,500 for married persons filing separately). Additional losses may be carried over to future years.
2. In 1987, the excess of net long-term capital gains over net short-term capital losses is included in taxable income, but the tax on such gains is limited.
3. Beginning in 1988, capital gains are treated like other types of income.
4. A capital asset is any item of property except:

   a. Inventories.
   b. Trade notes and accounts receivable.
   c. Real property and depreciable property used in a trade or business.
   d. Copyrights, letters and similar property.

IV. Corporation income tax

A. Dividend exclusion—a corporation may deduct the first 80% of dividends received from stock it owns in other domestic corporations.
B. Capital gains—long-term capital gains are subject to a top tax rate of 34% in 1987.
C. Tax rate—is progressive in just three steps.
D. Proprietorship or partnership income is included in the income of the proprietor or partners. (The proprietorship or partnership does not pay tax.)
E. Corporation income is taxed at corporation rates, and any portion paid in dividends is taxed again as individual income to its stockholders.

V. Tax effects of business alternatives

A. Method of financing

1. When a corporation is in need of additional financing, a tax advantage may be gained if owners supply funds through long-term loans instead of by purchasing stock.
2. Interest on borrowed funds is a tax-deductible expense; dividends are a distribution of earnings.

B. Timing transactions—can be important in tax planning

1. Taxpayers using cash method have flexibility in timing income and deductions.
2. Tax Reform Act of 1986 placed restrictions on availability of cash method.

C. Tax-free exchange occurs when:

1. Like kinds of property are exchanged for each other, or
2. One or more persons transfer property to a corporation and immediately thereafter are in control of the corporation.

D. Accounting basis and procedures

1. Whatever basis (cash or accrual) is used by taxpayers in keeping their records must also be used in computing taxable income.
2. Procedures must clearly reflect income and be consistently followed.

VI. Taxes and the distortion of net income

   A. Financial statements for a business are prepared in accordance with generally accepted accounting principles, while tax accounting is done in accordance with tax laws.
   B. GAAP requires that income taxes be allocated so that distortions caused by timing differences between tax accounting procedures and financial accounting procedures are avoided.
   C. Adjusting entries are used to record deferred income taxes.

Part I

Many of the important ideas and concepts discussed in Chapter 28 are reflected in the following list of key terms. Test your understanding of these terms by matching the appropriate definitions with the terms. Record the number identifying the most appropriate definition in the blank space next to each term.

_____ Accelerated cost recovery system (ACRS)

_____ Adjusted gross income

_____ Basis

_____ Capital asset

_____ Capital gain or loss

_____ Deferred income taxes

_____ Earned income

_____ Gross income

_____ Head of household

_____ Internal Revenue Code

_____ Marginal tax rate

_____ Standard deduction

_____ Tax avoidance

_____ Tax credit

_____ Tax evasion

_____ Tax planning

1. The rate that applies to the next dollar of income to be earned.

2. The difference between the income tax expense in the financial statements and the income taxes payable according to tax law, resulting from temporary differences between financial accounting and tax accounting with respect to expense or revenue recognition.

3. Evaluating the alternative ways in which business transactions can be structured in terms of the resulting tax liability and selecting the alternatives that will be most profitable.

4. A unique, accelerated depreciation method prescribed in the tax law.

5. A deduction from adjusted gross income that an individual may claim as an alternative to itemizing his or her personal deductions.

6. The difference between the proceeds from the sale of a capital asset and the basis of the asset.

7. The fraudulent denial and concealment of an existing tax liability.

8. An unmarried or legally separated person who maintains a home in which lives his or her unmarried child or a qualifying dependent.

9. A direct, dollar for dollar reduction in the amount of tax liability.

10. Gross income minus ordinary and necessary expenses of carrying on a business, trade, or profession as a self-employed person.

11. A legal means of preventing a tax liability from coming into existence.

12. In general, the cost of a purchased asset less any depreciation previously allowed or allowable for tax purposes.

13. Any item of property except (1) inventories, (2) trade notes and accounts receivable, (3) real property and depreciable property used in a trade or business, and (4) copyrights or similar property.

14. Collectively, the statutes dealing with taxation that have been adopted by Congress.

15. All income from whatever source derived, unless expressly excluded from taxation by law.

16. Wages, professional fees, and certain compensation for personal services.

Part II

Complete the following by filling in the blanks.

1. During 1987, the long-term capital gains of a corporation are subject to a top tax rate of
_____ %.

2. Common examples of capital assets held by individuals and subject to sale or exchange are
_____ .

3. A business executive _____ (will, will not) always be better off taxwise with his or her business organized as a corporation instead of a single proprietorship.

4. In 1987, a single individual whose only other income was a $55,000 salary had $10,000 of net long-term capital gains in excess of net short-term losses. The tax on the $10,000 gain will be $ _____ .

5. _____ taxpayers lose the benefit of the exemption deduction beginning in 1988.

6. Federal income tax rates for individuals generally are progressive in nature. By this is meant
_____ .

7. Federal tax rates for a corporation in 1988 are _____ % of income up to $50,000, _____ % of income from $50,000 to $75,000, and _____ % of income in excess of $75,000.

8. All income from whatever source derived, unless expressly excluded by law, is included in _____ income.

9. A business organized as a corporation must file a tax return and pay taxes on its taxable income. Also, if it pays out some of its "after-tax income" as dividends, its stockholders must report these dividends as _____ on their tax returns. Because of this, it is commonly claimed that corporation income is taxed
_____ .

10. The deduction for exemptions in 1988 amounts to $ _____ per exemption.

11. The standard deduction in 1988 for married persons filing a joint return is $ _____ , for a married person filing a separate return is $ _____ , and for a single taxpayer is $ _____ .

12. The answers to two questions are required in determining whether an item should be included or excluded from gross income for tax purposes. The questions are: _____
_____
_____ .

13. A business organized as a single proprietorship or a partnership is not required to pay federal income taxes; rather the income of such a business is taxed as _____
_____ .

14. Taxpayers should elect to deduct the _____
if its amount exceeds their itemized deductions.

15. The fraudulent denial and concealment of an existing tax liability is called tax _____
_____ and is illegal.

16. Good tax planning prevents a tax liability from _____
    _____ . It is legal and desirable and results in tax
    _____ .

17. To do tax planning, a taxpayer must be aware of the alternative choices available under the
    tax laws and select those that are _____ .

18. Net income and taxable income commonly differ because net income is determined by the
    application of _____ ,
    while tax _____ are used in determining taxable income, and the two
    differ on some points.

19. Generally accepted accounting principles require that income taxes be allocated and
    reported on a concern's income statements in such a manner that any distortions resulting
    from _____ are removed from the statements.

20. A cash-basis taxpayer sometimes can avoid income taxes by shifting _____
    _____ and _____ from
    one year to the next.

21. It _____ (is, is not) always to a taxpayer's advantage to exchange
    properties in such a manner as to secure a tax-free exchange.

Solutions for Chapter 28

Part I

Part II

1. 34%
2. stocks, bonds, and a personal residence
3. will not
4. $2,800
5. High-income
6. that each additional bracket of taxable income is taxed at a higher rate
7. 15%, 25%, 34%
8. gross
9. ordinary income, twice
10. $1,950
11. $5,000, $2,500, $3,000
12. Is the item income? Is it expressly excluded by law?
13. the individual income of the proprietor or partners
14. standard deduction
15. evasion
16. coming into existence, avoidance
17. most profitable
18. generally accepted accounting principles, laws
19. timing differences
20. revenues, expenses
21. is not